The Life and Fables of Aesop

The Life and Fables of

ÆSOP

A selection from the version
of Sir Roger L'Estrange
with fifty-three 15th century
woodcut illustrations
Edited by Simon Stern

 READERS UNION
LONDON W.C.2

KAHN & AVERILL

First published in Great Britain in 1970 by
Stanmore Press Ltd,
25 Thurloe Street, London SW7

© this edition Stanmore Press Ltd 1970

SBN 900707 05 4

Set in Linotype Pilgrim and Monotype Joanna
Printed in Great Britain
by Willmer Brothers Limited, Birkenhead

Contents

Introduction

Sɪʀ Roger L'Estrange's *Fables of Aesop and other Mythologists* from which this selection is taken, together with the second volume *Fables and Storyes Moralized*, form one of the most extensive collections of fables in existence. They were first published in 1692 and in addition to the *Life of Aesop*, which is reproduced here in full, they contain nearly eight hundred fables in all, two hundred of which are ascribed to Aesop. L'Estrange followed each fable with a lengthy *Moral Reflexion* expressing his own political and philosophical views. These *Reflexions* have been omitted here, as they are of little interest to the general reader.

Sir Roger L'Estrange was born in 1616 and died aged 84 after a turbulent life as a Tory journalist and pamphleteer in one of the most eventful periods of English history. At twenty-three he went with the army of Charles I to Scotland. Five years later, having planned to recapture Lynn for the Royalists and been betrayed by two confederates, he was sentenced to death by the Parliamentarians and remained in Newgate prison for over three years in 'a distressing condition of expectancy'. When he was thought no longer dangerous he was allowed to escape, and promptly organised a Royalist rising in Kent. The attempt was a fiasco and he fled to Holland under a cloud from both sides.

He managed to make his peace with Cromwell, and when the Restoration came, his vigorous diatribes against the freedom of the press earned him the post of *Surveyor of the Imprimerie*. In this capacity he published two newspapers, carried out a great many raids on printing offices and continued pamphleteering on behalf of the King; but in 1680 he was in trouble again. His attempts to discredit Titus Oates and the 'Popish Plot' misfired, and for his pains L'Estrange found himself accused of complicity in the 'plot'. Although he was acquitted, public opinion was so enraged that he was forced to leave the country. He was burned in effigy by the London mob and nick-named 'The Dog Towzer', which stuck for the rest of his life.

After a few months L'Estrange returned to England, faced out the storm, and started his most important venture in political journalism, 'The Observator'. In this news-sheet, published three or four times a week, L'Estrange violently attacked the Whigs and the Dissenters. 'The Observator' was much satirised and plagiarised in his own lifetime and was well-known to Defoe, Addison and Steele. Five years later L'Estrange's strong opposition to the Act of Indulgences brought him into conflict with his own government and the paper was suppressed.

This ironic event marked the decline of L'Estrange's fortunes. He spent another period in prison when the Whigs came to power, and in 1692 nearly died of an attack of apoplexy. However, three years later, at the age of 75, he was in sufficiently good health to be suspected of complicity in Fenwick's plot and was sent to prison yet again, but released after two months.

L'Estrange was short of money all his life and relied mainly on his pen for a living. His wife, Mary, was a compulsive gambler. On her death L'Estrange wrote: 'Play and gaming company have been the ruin of her wretched self, her husband and her family ... but ... after all never any creature lost a dearer wife'. He had a daughter who caused him great embarrassment by becoming a Catholic, and a son, Roger, who survived him by only five months.

His chief non-political work, apart from the *Aesop* for which he is best known today, is *The Works of Flavius Josephus compared with the original Greek*. He also translated Quevedo's *Visions* and *The Decameron* from the Spanish, and a number of works from the French, some of rather dubious nature. He was a keen amateur musician and patron of music and 'had a tolerable perfection on the base-viol'.

L'Estrange's vigorous and colloquial style was partly a reflection of his own nature and partly a conscious attempt to make himself intelligible to all classes. Boyer, a contemporary biographer, called him 'a very great Master of the English Tongue', but some critics accused him of corrupting the English language with his 'pert and affected phrases' and objected to his simplified spelling (so near to the spelling of today that it has not been necessary to alter it in this selection). L'Estrange was certainly a careless grammarian and a far from literal translator; but the fact remains that even after two hundred years his version of *Aesop* is still the most entertaining and readable that we have.

The woodcuts illustrating this book are reproduced from a Latin and Italian edition of *Aesop* published in Naples in 1485 by Francisco del Tuppo. They are superb examples of early book illustration, full of wit and strongly composed. Although they are 'naif' in style, with their giant insects, strange flowering trees and unlikely-looking animals, the draughtsmanship is confident and very accomplished. Nothing is known for sure about the identity of the artist. Judging from his angular style and his emphasis on the inner contours of the face, he probably came from Spain or Northern Europe. The illustrations to the *Fables* are gentler and more Italian in manner than those to the *Life of Aesop*, for which he would have had no Italian models. The borders, though clearly cut by the same artist, are completely Italian in style and may have been designed by someone else. The figures in their entablatures are Hercules wrestling with Antaeus, Samson and the lion, and two pygmies in combat mounted on mythical beasts.

As for Aesop himself, he is even more of a mystery. It seems probable that there really was an historical Aesop, and that his name and exploits became incorporated into folklore so that every fable was automatically attributed to him. Modern scholarship knows little more than was known in L'Estrange's day, and so we can do no better than to quote from his own preface.

We have had the History of Aesop so many times over and over, and dress'd up so many several Ways; that it would be but Labour-Lost to Multiply Unprofitable Conjectures upon a Tradition of so Great Uncertainty. Writers are divided about him, almost to all manner of purposes: And particularly concerning the Authority, even of the greater part of Those Compositions that pass the World in his Name: For, the Story is come down to us so Dark and Doubtful, that it is Impossible to Distinguish the Original from the Copy: And to say, which of the Fables are Aesop's, and which not; which are Genuine, and which Spurious: Beside, that there are divers Inconsistencies upon the Point of Chronology, in the Account of his Life, (as Maximus Planudes, and Others have Deliver'd it) which the whole Earth can never Reconcile ... This is enough in All Conscience, to Excuse any Man from laying over-much Stress upon the Historical Credit of a

Relation, that comes so Blindly, and so Variously Transmitted to us: Over and above that it is not one jot to our Bus'ness (further than to Gratify an Idle Curiosity) whether the Fact *be* True *or* False; *whether the* Man *was* Streight, *or* Crooked; *and his* Name, Aesop *or,* (*as some will have*) Lochman: *In all which Cases, the Reader is left at Liberty to Believe his Pleasure. We are not here upon the* Name, *the* Person, *or the* Adventures *of this Great Man; but upon the Subject of his* Apologues *and* Morals; *And not of* His *alone, but of several other Eminent Men that have Written after his Copy; and abundantly Contributed in those Labours, to the Delight, Benefit, and Instruction of Those that were to come after them.*

SIMON STERN

The Life of Aesop

Chapter one: Of Aesop's Country, Condition and Person

AESOP (according to *Planudes, Camerarius* and Others) was by birth of *Ammorius*, a Town in the *Greater Phrygia;* (though some will have him to be a *Thracian*, others a *Samian*); of a mean Condition, and his person deformed to the highest degree: Flat-Nos'd, Hunch-Back'd, Blobber-Lipp'd; a Long Mishapen Head; His Body Crooked all over, Big-Belly'd, Baker-Legg'd, and his Complexion so swarthy that he took his very Name from't; for *Aesop* is the same with *Aethiop*. And he was not only Unhappy in the most scandalous Figure of a Man that ever was heard of; but he was in a manner Tongue-Ty'd too, by such an Impediment in his speech, that People could very hardly understand what he said. This Imperfection is said to have been the most sensible part of his Misfortune; for the Excellency of his Mind might otherwise have Atton'd in some Measure for the Uncouth Appearance of his Person (at least if That Part of his History may pass for Current.) There goes a Tradition, that he had the good Hap to Relieve certain Priests that were Hungry and out of their way, and to set them Right again; and that for that good Office he was, upon their Prayers, brought to the Use of his Tongue: But *Camerarius*, whom I shall Principally follow, has no Faith in the Miracle, And so he begins his History with the tracing of him to *Samos*, and from thence Prosecutes it through the most Remarkable Passages of his Life, to the Last Barbarous Violence upon him at Delphos. As to his Impediment in his Speech, whether there were any such thing or Not, or how he came to be cur'd of it, the Reader is at Liberty what to Believe and what Not. And so likewise for Twenty Other Passages up and down this History: Some of them too Trivial, and others too Gross, to be taken Notice of Upon this Argument and Occasion: Let it suffice that (according to the Common Tradition) he had been Already Twice Bought and Sold; and so we shall Date the Story of his Adventures from his Entrance into the Service of at least a Third Master.

As to the Age he liv'd in, it is Agreed upon among the Antients that it was when *Croesus* Govern'd *Lydia*; as also that *Xanthus*, a *Samian*, was his Master. *Herodotus* will have it to be one *Jadmon* a *Samian* too; but still according to the Current of most Writers, *Xanthus* was the Man.

Chapter two: Aesop and his Fellow-Slaves Upon their Journey to Ephesus

IT was *Aesop's* Fortune to be sent to *Ephesus*, in Company with other Slaves to be sold. His Master had a great many Burdens to Carry, and *Aesop* begg'd of his Companions not to over Charge him. They found him a Weakling, and bad him please himself. The Parcel that he Pitch'd upon was a Panier of Bread; and twice as heavy as any of the rest. They called him a thousand Fools for his pains, and so took up their Luggage, and away they Trudg'd together. About Noon, they had their Dinner deliver'd out of *Aesop's* Basket, which made his Burden Lighter by one half in the Afternoon than it had been in the Morning. And after the next Meal he had nothing left him to Carry but an Empty Basket. His Fellow-Slaves began Now to Understand that *Aesop* was not so Arrant a Fool as they took him for; and that they Themselves had not half the Wit they Thought they had.

18

Chapter three: Aesop is accus'd by False Witnesses for Stealing his Master's Figs; and brings himself off by his Wits, to the Confusion of his Accusers

AESOP was not of a *Make* to do his Master much credit in the Quality of a *Houshold Servant:* So that he rather sent him abroad into the *Fields* a Digging, and to take care of his *Husbandry.* By the time he had been there a While, his Master went out after him to see how he went on with his Work; and found Every thing done much to his Satisfaction. In this *Interim* comes a Country-man to him with a Present of most Delicious *Figs;* which he was so Wonderfully delighted with, that he gave them in Charge to his Boy *Agathopus* to see them carefully laid up till he came back again from the *Bath,* whither he was then a going. *Aesop,* it seems, was now gone home upon some Particular Business, and *Agathopus* laid hold of This Occasion to tell One of his Companions of a Design he had, both upon the *Figs,* and upon their *Fellow-Servant.* *What have we more to do,* says he, *than to Stuff our Guts with these* Figs *our selves, and then lay the Roguery upon* Aesop, *who is at This Instant in the House where they are? And then, when our Master comes to Examine the Matter, we are Two Witnesses to One against him, which will make it so clear a Case, that the Silly Cur will not have the Face to Deny the Fact.* The Plot, in short, was agreed upon; and to

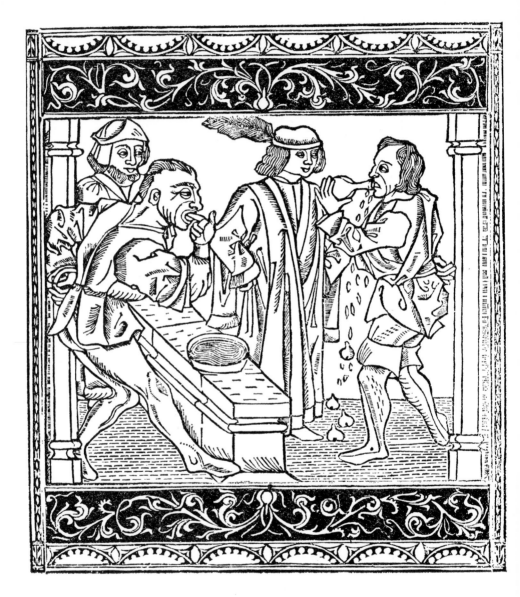

20

work they went upon the *Figs*, making themselves Merry upon Every Bit they Swallow'd, to Consider how *Aesop's* Carcass was to pay for All.

The Master, upon his coming from the *Bath*, call'd immediately for his Figs, and hearing that *Aesop* had been beforehand with him, sent for him in a Rage, and Rattled him with a Thousand *Traytors* and *Villains*, for Robbing his House and Devouring the Fruit that he had set apart for his own Palate. This Miserable Wretch heard and understood All that was said; but, by Reason of an Imperfection in his Speech, he was not able to speak one Word in his Own Defence. His Enemies in the mean time Insulting over him, and calling for *Justice* upon so Insolent a Cheat. They were now advancing from Reproches to Blows, When *Aesop* cast himself at his Master's Feet, and begg'd his Patience only till he might go out, and come in again. He went his way immediately, and fetch'd a Vessel of Warm Water; took a Large Draught of it, in his Master's Presence, and with his Finger in his Throat brought it all Clear up again without any Other Mixture. After This Experiment upon *Himself*, he gave his Master to Understand, that if he would be pleased to put his *Accusers* to the same *Test*, he should quickly see what was become of his *Figs*. The Proposal seem'd so Reasonable, that he Order'd *Agathopus* and his *Fellow* to do the Like. They made some Difficulty at first of following *Aesop's* Example; but in the end, upon taking a Soup of the same Liquor, their Stomachs Wambled, and up came the *Water*, *Figs and All*. Upon This Evidence of the Treachery and Falshood of *Agathopus* and his *Companion*, the Master Order'd them to be Soundly Lash'd, and made good the Old Saying, *Harm Watch, Harm Catch*.

Chapter four: The Sale of Aesop to Xanthus

UPON the Merchants Arrival at *Ephesus*, he made a quick Riddance of All his Slaves but Three, That is to say, a *Musician*, an *Orator*, and *Aesop*. He dress'd up the Two Former in Habits answerable to their Profession, and Carry'd them to *Samos*, as the Likeliest Place for a Chapman. He shew'd them there in the open Market, with *Aesop* for a Fool betwixt them; which some People took much offence at. While they were attending upon the Place, there came, among other *Samians*, one *Xanthus*, an Eminent Philosopher of that City, with a Train of his Disciples at his Heels. The Philosopher was mightily pleased with the Two Youths, and ask'd them one after another about their Profession, and what they could do. The one told him he could do *any thing*, the other that he could do *ev'ry thing*; this set *Aesop* a laughing at 'em. The Philosopher's Pupils would Needs know what it was that made *Aesop* so merry. Why says he, if the Question had been put by your Master, I should have told him the reason of it.

Xanthus in the mean time was beating the Price of the Two other Slaves, but the Terms were so high, that he was just upon turning about to go his way, Only the Pupils would needs have him put the same Questions first to the Ill favour'd Fellow, that he had done to the other Two; and so *Xanthus*, for the Humour sake, Interrogated *Aesop* what *He* could do. *Nothing at all*, says he. How comes That says the Philosopher? My Companions, says the Other, Undertake every thing,

23

and there's Nothing left for me to do. This gave them to Understand, that the Man knew well enough what he said, and what he Laugh'd at. Well! says *Xanthus*, but if I should give Money for you Now, would you be Good and Honest? I'll be That, says *Aesop* whether you Buy me or No. Ay, but tell me again says the Philosopher Won't you run away? Pray, says *Aesop*, did you ever hear of a Bird in a Cage, that told his Master he Intended to make his Escape; *Xanthus* was well enough pleased with the Turn and Quickness of his Wit; but, says he, That Unlucky Shape of yours will set People a Hooting and Gaping at you where-ever you go. A Philosopher, says *Aesop*, should value a Man for his Mind, Not for his Body. This presence of Thought gave *Xanthus* a High Opinion of the Wisdom of the Man; and so he bad the Merchant set him his Lowest Price of That Miserable Creature. Why says he, you had as good Cheapen a Dunghil; but if you'll bid me like a Chapman for either of the Other Two, you shall have this Phantome into the Bargain. Very good says the Philosopher; and without any more ado what's your selling Price? The Merchant speaks the Word, The Philosopher pays the Money, and takes *Aesop* away with him.

Chapter five: Xanthus presents Aesop to his Wife

Xanthus had no sooner made his Purchase, and carry'd his Jewel home with him, but, having a kind of a Nice Froward Piece to his Wife, the Great Difficulty was how to put her in humour for the Entertainment of this Monster, without throwing the House out at the Window. My Dear, says he, You have been often complaining of Careless Servants; And I have brought you one Now that I am Confident will fit your Turn. He shall Go and Come, and Wait, and do Every thing as you would have him; Oh, your Servant Sweet heart, says she, but what did he cost you? Why truly very Reasonable; but at Present He's a Little Tann'd, and out of case you must know, with his Journey, says the Husband, and so he Order'd him to be call'd in. The Cunning Gipsy smoak'd the Matter presently. Some Monster says she, I'll be Hanged else. Wife, Wife, says *Xanthus*, If you are a good Woman, That that Pleases Me Must Please You too. While These Words were between his Lips, up comes *Aesop* towards them; she gave him a Fierce Look, and Immediately discharg'd her Choler upon her Husband. Is this a *Man*, or a *Beast?* says she, and what Clearer Proof in the World Could You have given me Now, of an Insufferable Hatred and Contempt; *Aesop* said not one Word all This While; 'till *Xanthus* Rouz'd him with a Reproof. O Villain! says he, to have a Tongue and Wit at Will upon All other Occasions, and not one Diverting Syllable Now at a Pinch, to Pacify your Mistress! *Aesop*, after a short Pause upon't Bolted out an old *Greek* Saying, which is in English to this Effect, *From Lying at the Mercy of Fire, Water, and a Wicked Woman, Good Lord deliver us*. If the Wife was heartily angry before, This Scomm made her Stark Mad, and the Reproche was so Cutting too, that *Xanthus* himself did not well know how to take it. But *Aesop* brought himself off again from the Malice of any ill Intention, by a Passage out of *Euripides* to this Purpose. *The Raging of a Tempestuous Sea; The Fury of a Devouring Fire, and the Pinching Want of Necessaries for Life, are Three Dreadful Things,* and a Body might reckon up a Thousand more; *But all this is Nothing to the Terrible Violences of an Impetuous Woman,* and therefore says he, Make your self as Glorious on the other side, in the Rank of Good Women.

Vavasor the Jesuite, in his Treatise *De Ludicra Distione*, takes Notice of a Blunder here in the Chronology of the Story. For *Aesop* was Murder'd at least Fourscore Years before *Euripides* was Born. But to follow the Thread of the Relation; Upon this Oblique Admonition, the Woman came to her self again. And took *Aesop* into her good Graces, who render'd his Master and Mistress All the Offices of a Faithful Servant.

Chapter six: Aesop's Answer to a Gard'ner

SOME Two or Three Days after the Encounter above mentioned, *Xanthus* took *Aesop* along with him to a Garden to buy some Herbs, and the *Gard'ner*, seeing him in a Habit of Philosopher, told him the Admiration he was in, to find how much faster Those Plants shot up that Grow of their own Accord, than Those that he set Himself, though he took never so much Care about them. Now you that are a Philosopher, Pray will you tell me the meaning of This? *Xanthus* had no better answer at hand, then to tell him, That Providence will have it so: Whereupon *Aesop* brake out into a Loud Laughter. Why how now Ye slave You, says *Xanthus*, what do you Laugh at? *Aesop* took him aside and told him, Sir, I Laugh at your Master, that Taught You no better: for what signifies a Gen'ral Answer to a Particular Question? And 'tis no News Neither that Providence orders All Things: But if you'll turn him over to me, You shall see I'll give him another sort of Resolve. *Xanthus* told the *Gard'ner*, that it was below a Philosopher to busy his head about such Trifles; but says he, If you have a Curiosity to be better Inform'd, you shall do well to ask my Slave here, and see what he'll say to you. Upon this, the *Gard'ner* put the Question to *Aesop*, Who gave him this Answer. The Earth is in the Nature of a *Mother* to what She brings forth of her Self, out of her own Bowels; Whereas She is only a kind of *Step-Dame*, in the Production of Plants that are Cultivated and Assisted by the Help and Industry of Another: so that it's Natural for

29

her to Withdraw her Nourishment from the One, towards the Relief of the Other. The *Gard'ner*, upon this, was so well satisfied, That he would take no Money for his Herbs, and desired *Aesop* to make Use of his Garden for the future, as if it were his own.

There are several Stories in *Planudes*, that I shall pass over in this place (says *Camerarius*) as not worth the while: Particularly the Fables of the *Lentills*, the *Bath*, the *Sow's Feet*, and several Little Tales and Jests that I take to be neither well Laid, nor well put together; Neither is it any matter, in Relations of this Nature, Whether they be True or False, but if they be Proper and Ingenious; and so contriv'd, that the Reader or the Hearer may be the better of them, That's as much as is required: Wherefore I shall now Commit to Writing Two Fables or Stories, One about the bringing his Mistress home again, when she had left her Husband; Which is drawn from the Model of a Greek History set out by *Pausanias* in his Description of *Boetia*; The Other, upon the Subject of a Treat of *Neats Tongues*, which was taken from *Bias*, as we have it from *Plutarch* in his *Convivium Septem Sapientum*.

Chapter seven: Aesop's Invention to bring his Mistress back again to her Husband, after she had Left him

THE Wife of *Xanthus* was well born and wealthy, but so Proud and Domineering withal, as if her Fortune and her Extraction had Entitled her to the Breeches. She was Horribly Bold, Medling, and *Expensive;* (as that sort of Women commonly are,) Easily put off the Hooks, and Monstrous hard to be pleased again: Perpetually chattering at her Husband, and upon All occasions of controversy, Threatning him to be gone. It came to this at Last, That *Xanthus's* stock of Patience being quite spent, he took up a Resolution of going another way to Work with her, and of trying a Course of Severity, since there was nothing to be done with her by Kindness. But this Experiment, instead of mending the matter, made it worse; for upon harder Usage, The Woman grew Desperate, and went away from him in Earnest. She was as Bad 'tis true as Bad might well be, and yet *Xanthus* had a kind of *Hankering* for her still: Beside that there was matter of Interest in the Case: and a Pestilent Tongue she had, that the Poor Husband Dreaded above all things under the Sun: but the Man was willing however to make the Best of a Bad Game, and so his Wits and his Friends were set at Work, in the fairest Manner that Might be, to get her home again. But there was No good to be done in't it seems; and *Xanthus* was so visibly out of Humour upon't, that *Aesop* in Pure Pity bethought himself Immediately how to Comfort him. Come Master (says he) Pluck up a good heart; for I have a Project in my Noddle that shall bring my Mistress to you back again, with as good a Will as ever she went from you. What does me *Aesop*, but away Immediately to the Market among the Butchers, Poulterers, Fishmongers, Confectioners, &c. for the Best of Every thing that was in Season. Nay he takes private People in his way too, and Chops into the very house of his Mistresses Relations, as by Mistake. This Way of Proceeding set the whole Town a Gog to know the Meaning of all this Bustle, and *Aesop* innocently told every body That his Master's Wife was run away from him, and he had Marry'd another: His Friends up and down were all Invited to come and make Merry with him, and This was to be the Wedding Feast. The News flew like lightning, and happy were they could carry the First Tydings of it to the *Run-away Lady:* (for every Body knew *Aesop* to be a Servant in that Family.) It Gather'd in the Rolling, as all other Stories do in the Telling: Especially where Womens Tongues and Passions have the spreading of them. The Wife that was in her Nature Violent, and Unsteady, order'd her Chariot to be made ready immediately, and away she Posts back to her Husband: falls upon him with Outrages of Looks and Language; and after the easing of her Mind a little; No *Xanthus*, says she, Do not you Flatter your self with the hopes of Enjoying another Woman while I am alive. *Xanthus* look'd upon this as one of *Aesop's* Masterpieces; and for that Bout all was well again betwixt Master and Mistress.

Chapter eight: An Entertainment of Neats Tongues

Some few days after the Ratification of this Peace, *Xanthus* Invited several Philosophers of his Acquaintance to Supper with him; and Charges *Aesop* to make the best Provision he could think of for their Entertainment. *Aesop* had a Wit Waggish Enough, and this General Commission furnish'd him with Matter to work upon. So soon as ever the Guests were set down at the Table, *Xanthus* calls for Supper, and expected no less than a very Splendid Treat. The first Service was *Neats Tongues* sliced, which the Philosophers took Occasion to Discourse and Quibble upon in a Grave Formal way, as *The Tongue* (for the purpose) *is the Oracle of Wisdom*, and the like. *Xanthus*, upon This, calls for a second Course, and after that for a third, and so for a fourth, which were All *Tongues*, over and over again still, only several ways Dressed: some Boiled, others Fryed, and some again serv'd up in Soupe, which put *Xanthus* into a Furious Passion. Thou Villain, says he, Is this according to my Order, to have nothing but *Tongues upon Tongues?* Sir says *Aesop*, without any hesitation, since it is my Ill fortune to fall under this Accusation, I do Appeal to All these Learned Persons, whether I have done Well, or Ill, and paid that Respect to your Order which I ought to do.

Your Order was, That I should make the Best Provision that I could think of for the Entertainment of these Excellent Persons, and if the *Tongue* be the Key that Leads Us into All *Knowledge*, what could be more proper and suitable then *a Feast of Tongues for a Philosophical Banquet?*

When *Xanthus* found the Sence of the Table to be on *Aesop's* side; Well my Friends, says he; Pray will You Eat with me to Morrow, and I'll try if I can mend your Chear; and Mr. *Major Domo*, says he to *Aesop*, let it be the Care of your Gravity and Wisdom to provide us a Supper to Morrow, of the very worst Things You can Think of.

Xanthus's Guests met again The Next day according to the Appointment; and *Aesop* had provided them the very same Services of *Tongues and Tongues over and over*, as they had the Night before. Sirrah (says *Xanthus* to his Servant) what's the Meaning of This, That *Tongues* should be the *Best* of Meats *One* Day, and the *Worst* the *Other?* Why Sir says he, There is not any Wickedness under the Sun, That the *Tongue* has not a part in. As Murders, Treasons, Violence, Injustice, Fraud, and All manner of Lewdness: For Counsels must be first Agitated, The Matter in Question Debated, Resolv'd upon, and Communicated by Words, before the Malice comes to be executed in fact. *Tongue whither wilt thou!* (says the Old Proverb) I go to *Build* (says the *Tongue*,) and I go to *pull down*.

This Petulant Liberty of *Aesop*, Gall'd his Master to the very Soul of him, and one of the Guests, to Help forward his Evil Humour, Cry'd out, *This Fellow is enough to make a Body Mad!* Sir (says *Aesop*) you have very little Business to do of your own I perceive, by the Leisure you have to Intermeddle in Other Peoples Matters: You would find some other Employment else, then to Irritate a Master against his Servant.

Chapter nine: Aesop brings his Master a Guest that had no sort of Curiosity in him

XANTHUS laid hold of the Present Occasion, and was willing enough to be furnished with a Staff to beat a Dog. Well Sirrah, says he, since this Learned Gentleman is too *Curious;* go you your ways and find me out a Man that has no Curiosity at All, or I'll Lace your Coat for ye. *Aesop,* the next day, Walked the whole Town over on this Errand; and at Last, found out a Slovenly Lazy Fellow, Lolling at his Ease, as if he had Nothing to do or to take care for; and so up to him he went in a Familiar Way; and Invited him to his Master's to Supper. The Clown made no Ceremony of promising, but fell Presently to asking what kind of Man his Master was? And what, says he, are we going just now? (for this Poor Devil look'd upon a Meal's Meat *Gratis* as a Blessing Dropt into his Mouth out of the Skies.) Come (says *Aesop*) we are going this very Moment; and Wonderfully Glad he was to find by the Booby's Discourse, That he had met with a Man so fit for his Purpose. Away they went together, and so strait into the Parlour, where the Blockhead throws Himself down Dirty and Beastly as he was, upon a Rich Couch. After a very little While, in comes *Xanthus* to Supper, and asks *Aesop* who that Man was? Why, This is the Man, says *Aesop*, that you sent me for; that is to say, a Man that has no *Curiosity* in him at All. Oh that's very well, says *Xanthus*, and then told his Wife in her ear, That if she would be but a Loving and Obedient Wife to him, and do as he bad her, he would now save her Longing, for, says he, I have been a Great while Seeking for an Occasion to pick a Quarrel with *Aesop*, and I have found it at last. After this Whisper, *Xanthus* takes a Turn in the Parlor, and calls aloud to his Wife, Hark ye Sweet Heart, says he, go fetch some Water, and Wash the Feet of my Guest here. Away she goes, brings a Bason to the side of the Couch, where the Clown was laid at his Length, and bad him put forth his Feet for her to Wash them. *Xanthus* little thought he would have done it. But the Clown, after a little Stumble within himself that 'twas fitter for the Maid to do't then the Mistress: Well, says he, If it be the Custom of the Family, 'tis not for me to be against it; and so he stretch'd forth his *Feet* to her *Washing*.

So soon as ever the Company had taken off the Edge of their Stomachs, *Xanthus* calls for a Bumper, and puts it into the hands of the Clown, making no doubt but he would have allow'd his Host the Honour of being his Taster. The Fellow, without any Scruple, Whips up the Drink, and *Xanthus* gives the Pot again Empty, who was now the second Time Disappointed upon the Matter of *Curiosity*, or *No Curiosity At All*. He had a Mind still to be upon poor *Aesop's Bones*, and made another Tryal of the Humour of his Guest. There was a particular Dish that the Clown fed very Heartily upon: *Xanthus* fell into a Rage with the Cook for Ill-Dressing of it, and Threat'ned to have him brought and Lash'd in the very Parlor. The *Bumpkin* took no Notice of it at All, but without speaking one Word on the Cook's Behalf, it was nothing to him he thought, what other People did with their Servants.

They were come Now to their Cakes and Pyes, and the Clown Guttled upon them without Mercy. *Xanthus* Resolves then upon Another Tryal; Calls for his *Pastry Cook* and tells him, Sirrah, says he, you spoil every thing that goes through your hands. There's neither Spice, nor any other Seasoning here. The Cook told him, That if they were either Over

or Under-Bak'd, it was his Fault; But for the Spice and Seasoning, it was his Mistresses, for it was All put in that she Deliver'd. Nay Wife, says *Xanthus*, if it sticks there, By All that's Sacred, I'll Treat you no better then if you were a Slave bought with my Money. Wherefore Strip

Immediately and Prepare for a Dog-Whip. *Xanthus* thought with himself that if any thing in the World could move this Barbarous Brute, he would have put in a Word at Least to save a Woman of Honour from so Scandalous an Indignity. But says this Loggerhead to himself; There's an Old Saying; *What have We to do to Quench other Peoples Fires?* And I'll e'en keep my self clear of other Peoples Matters; Only he took *Xanthus* by the Hand indeed, and told him if he would but stay a Little, he'd go fetch his own Wife too, and so they might take the Lash by Turns. In one word, *Xanthus* missed his Aim at last; and though he was troubled at the Miscarriage, he could not but Laugh yet at the Simplicity of the Man, and Confess that *Aesop* was in the Right, in bringing a Person to him that had no Curiosity at all.

Chapter ten: Aesop's Answer to a Magistrate

IT happened some few days after the Last Passage above, that *Xanthus*, having some Business at the Publick Hall, sent *Aesop* to see if there were any Great Throng of Men there; a Magistrate meets him Upon the *Way*, and Asks him whither he was going? Why truly, says *Aesop*, I am going I know not whither. The Magistrate took it that he Banter'd him, and bad an Officer take him into Custody and Carry him to Prison. Well, says *Aesop*, to the Magistrate; Is it not true Now, that I did not know Whither I was going? Can you imagine that when I came out of the House this Morning, I had any thoughts of going to Prison? The Magistrate was well enough pleased at the Fancy, and Discharg'd him Upon it, and so he went forward to the Hall; Where, among a world of People, he saw one Man Arrest another upon an Action of Debt. The Debtor Pleaded Poverty; but if he would Compound for half, it should go hard but he'd make a shift to pick it up, he said. Well, with all my Heart, says the Creditor, Lay down the Money upon the Nail, and the Business is done: for a Man had better Content himself with Half, then Lose All. And I reckon on that Money as good as lost, that a Man must go to Law for; *Aesop*, upon this, went back and told his Master, that he had been at the Hall, and saw but one Man there; This was a Riddle to *Xanthus*; Insomuch that he went himself to Learn the Truth of the Matter. When he came to the Place, he found the Court extremely Thronged, and turning short upon *Aesop*, in great Indignation,

Sirrah, says he, are all these People come since you told me there was but one Man here? 'This very true, says *Aesop*, there was a Huge Crowd, and yet but *one Man* that I could see in that vast *Multitude*. This seems to be taken out of the Life of *Diogenes*.

Chapter eleven: Xanthus undertakes to Drink the Sea Dry

THERE happened, not long after This, to be a Merry Meeting of Philosophers; and *Xanthus*, one of the Company. *Xanthus* had already gotten a Cup too much; and *Aesop* finding they were like to set out his hand; Sir, says he, 'tis the Humour of *Bacchus*, they say, first to make Men *Chearful*, and when they are past That, to make 'em *Drunk*, and in the Conclusion, to make them *Mad*. *Xanthus* took Offence at *Aesop*; and told him, That was a Lecture for Children. (*Laertius* makes this to be the saying of *Anacharsis*.) The Cups went round, and *Xanthus* by this Time had taken his Load, who was mightily given to talk in his Drink; and whatever was uppermost, out it came without either Fear or Wit. One of the Company observing the weak side of the Man, took the Opportunity of Pumping him, with several Questions. *Xanthus* (says he) I have read some-where, that it is possible for a Man to Drink the Sea Dry; but I can hardly believe it. Why says *Xanthus*, I'll venture my House and Land upon't, that I do't my-self. They Agreed upon the Wager, and presently off went their Rings to Seal the Conditions. But Early the next Morning *Xanthus* missing his Ring, thought it might be slipt off his Finger, and ask'd *Aesop* about it. Why truly says *Aesop*, I can say Nothing to the Losing of your *Ring;* But I can tell you that *you Lost your House and Land last Night:* and so *Aesop* told him the Story on't, which his Master it seems had utterly forgotten. *Xanthus* began now to Chew upon the Matter, and it went to the Heart of him to

Consider That he could neither do the thing, nor yet get quit of his Bonds. In this trouble of Thoughts he Consults *Aesop*, (whose advice before he had rejected) what was to be done in this Case. I shall never forget, says *Xanthus* how much I owe you for your Faithful Services; and so with fair Words *Aesop* was prevail'd upon to Undertake the bringing of him off. 'Tis Impossible to do the Thing, (says he) but if I can find a way to Dissolve the Obligation, and to gain you Credit by it over and Above, That's the Point I suppose will do your Business. The Time appointed, says *Aesop*, is now at hand, Wherefore do you set a bold Face upon it, and go to the *Sea-side* with all your Servants and your Trinkets about you, and put on a Countenance that you are just Now about to make good your Undertaking. You'll have Thousands of Spectators there, and when they are got together, let the Form of the Agreement and the Condition be Read, which runs to this Effect. That you are to Drink up the Sea by such a certain Time, or to Forfeit your House and Land, upon such and such a Consideration. When this is done, call for a Great Glass, and let it be fill'd with *Sea-Water*, in the Sight of the Whole Multitude: Hold it up then in your Hand, and say as Follows, *You have heard Good People, what I have undertaken to do, and upon what Penalty, if I do not go through with it. I confess the Agreement, and the Matter of Fact as you have heard it; and I am now about to drink up the Sea; not the Rivers that run into't. And therefore let all the Inlets be stopt, that there be nothing but pure Sea left me to drink, and I am now ready to perform my part of the Agreement. But for any drinking of the Rivers, There is nothing of that in the Contract.* The People found it so clear a Case, That they did not only agree to the Reason and Justice of *Xanthus*'s Case, but Hiss'd his Adversary out of the Field; Who in the Confusion made a Publique Acknow-

43

ledgment, that *Xanthus* was the Wiser and Better Man of the Two; but desired the Contract might be made void, and offer'd to Submit Himself further to such Arbitrators as *Xanthus* Himself should direct. *Xanthus* was so well pleased with the Character his Adversary had given him, of a Wise Man, That all was Passed over, and a final End made of the Dispute. *Plutarch* makes this to have been the Invention of *Bias*.

Chapter twelve: Aesop Baffles the Superstition of Augury

IN the days of *Aesop*, The World was mightily addicted to *Augury;* that is to say, to the gathering of *Omens* from the Cry and Flight of *Birds.* Upon this Account it was, that *Xanthus* one Day sent *Aesop* into the Yard, and bad him look well about him. If you see *Two Crows* (says he) you'll have *good Luck* after it, but if you should chance to spy *One Crow Single*, 'tis a *Bad Omen*, and some Ill will betide you. *Aesop* stept out and came Immediately back again, and told his Master that he had seen *Two Crows.* Hereupon *Xanthus* went out Himself, and finding but *One* (for the Other was flown away) he fell Outragiously upon *Aesop* for making Sport with him, and Order'd him to be soundly Lash'd for't, but just as they were stripping him for the Execution, in comes One to Invite *Xanthus* abroad to Supper. Well Master, says *Aesop*, and where's the Credit of your *Augury* Now? When I, that saw *Two Crows*, am to be beaten like a Dog, and You, that saw but *One*, are going to *make Merry* with your Friends? The Reason and Quickness of this Reflexion Pacify'd the Master for the present, and sav'd the Poor Fellow a sound whipping.

Chapter thirteen: Aesop finds hidden Treasure

As *Xanthus* was walking once among certain Monuments, with *Aesop* at his Heels, and Plodding upon several *Epitaphs*, there was one Inscription in *Greek Letters*, that *Xanthus* with all his skill he had, could not tell what to make of. Well, says *Aesop*, let me see a little if I can Uncypher it. And so after laying Things and Things together a while, Master, says he, What will you give me, if I find you out a Pot of Hidden Treasure Now? One *Half* of it, says *Xanthus*, and your Liberty. So *Aesop* fell to Digging, a matter of four Yards from the Stone that had the Inscription; and there found a Pot of Gold which he took up and Deliver'd to his Master; and Claim'd his Promise. Well, says *Xanthus*, I'll be as good as my Word; but you must first shew me how you came to know there was Treasure, by the Inscription: for I had rather be Master of that Secret, than of the very Gold it self. *Aesop* innocently open'd the whole Matter to him. Look you Sir, says he, Here are these Letters. $a; \beta; \delta; o; \epsilon; \theta; \chi;$ which are to be thus Interpreted; a stands for $\dot{a}\pi o\beta\dot{a}s$; β for $\beta\acute{\eta}\mu a\tau a$; δ for $\delta\acute{\epsilon}\sigma\sigma a\rho a$; o for $\dot{o}\rho\acute{\upsilon}\xi as$; ϵ for $\epsilon\dot{\upsilon}\rho\acute{\epsilon}\sigma\epsilon\iota s$; θ for $\theta\eta\sigma a\upsilon\rho\dot{o}\nu$; χ for $\chi\rho\upsilon\sigma\acute{\iota}o\nu$. In English, *Dig four Paces from this Place, and you shall find Gold*. Now says *Xanthus*, if you are so good at finding out Gold, you and I must not part yet. Come Sir, says *Aesop*, (perceiving that his Master plaid fast and loose with him) To deal freely with you, This Treasure belongs to King *Dionysius*. How do you know that? says *Xanthus*. Why by the very Inscription, says *Aesop;* for in that Sence

a stands for ἀπόδος; $β$ for βασιλει; $δ$ for Διονυσίῳ; o for ὄν; $ε$ for εὗρες; $θ$ for θησαυρὸν; $χ$ for χρυσίον. In English, *Give* Dionysius *the Gold you have found.* Xanthus began to be afraid when he heard it was the King's Money, and Charg'd *Aesop* to make no Words on't, and he should have the one half. 'Tis well, says *Aesop;* but this is not so much your own Bounty yet, as the Intention of Him that Bury'd it; for the very same Letters direct the Dividing of it. As for Example once again now, a stands for ἀνελόμενοι; $β$ for βαδίσαντες; $δ$ for δίελεατε; o for ὄν; $ε$ for εὕρετε; $θ$ for θησαυρὸν; $χ$ for χρυσίον; In English, *divide the Gold that you have found.* Why then, says *Xanthus,* let us go home and share it. No sooner were they got home, but *Aesop* was presently laid by the Heels, for fear of Blabbing, crying out as loud as he could, this comes of trusting to the Faith of a Philosopher; The Reproach Nettled his Master: but however he caused his Shackles to be taken off upon't, and Admonished *Aesop* to keep his Licentious Tongue in a little better Order for the future, if ever he hoped to have his Liberty. For That, says *Aesop,* Prophetically, I shall not need to beg it of you as a Favour, for in a very few days I shall have my Freedom, whether you will or no.

Chapter fourteen: Aesop Expounds upon an Augury, and is made Free

AESOP had thus far born All the Indignities of a Tedious Slavery with the Constancy of a Wise Man, and without either Vanity or Abjection of Mind. He was not Ignorant however of his own Value; neither did he neglect any Honest Way or Occasion of Advancing his Name and his Credit in the World; as in One particular Instance among the *Samians*, on a Strange Thing that happen'd There upon a Very Solemn Day. The Ring, it seems, that had the Town-Seal upon't was laid somewhere in sight, Where an Eagle could come at it; she took it up in the Air, and dropt it into the Bosom of a Slave. The *Samians* took this for a Fore-boding, that Threaten'd some dismal Calamity to the State, and in a General Consternation they presently call'd a Council of their Wise Men; and *Xanthus* in the first Place, to give their Opinions upon This Mysterious Accident. They were all at a Loss what to Think on't, only *Xanthus* desired some few days time for further Consideration. Upon This, he betook himself to his Study, and the more he Beat his Brains about it, the further he found himself from any hope of Expounding the Secret. This put him into a deep Melancholy; which made *Aesop* very Importunate, and Impatient, to know the Cause of it; with Assurances, That he would serve his Master in The Affair, Whatever it was, to the Uttermost of his Power. *Xanthus* hereupon laid the whole Matter before him, and told him in Conclusion, that he was not only lost in his Reputation, but in Danger to be Torn to Pieces by the Rabble. When *Aesop* found how the Case stood, never trouble your Head any further, says he, Do but follow my Advice, and I'll bring you off as well now as ever I did before. When you Appear to Morrow to give your Answer, I would have you speak to the People after this Manner.

I need not tell your Wisdoms, That so Many Heads, so many Minds, and so many several Men, so many several Conceptions of Things; Nay, and further, that every several Art, or Profession requires a distinct Faculty or Disposition, that is more or less Peculiar to it self. It is the Custom of the World for People in all Cases where they are either Ignorant or Doubtful, to repair to Men that have the Reputation of Philosophers, for Counsel and Satisfaction. But this under favour, is a great Mistake; for it is with Philosophers, as it is, I say, with other Arts and Professions that have their Functions apart the one from the other. Wisdom 'tis true, may be call'd properly enough the Knowledge of things Divine and Humane, but will you therefore expect that a Philosopher should do the Office of a Shoemaker or a Barber, because the Trades are conversant about human things? No no Gentlemen, a Man may be a Great Philosopher without any Skill at all in the handling the Awl, or the Razor. But if the Question were concerning the Government of Life and Manners, the Nature of things Coelestial or Terrestrial; The Duties that we owe to God or Man; you could not do better than repair to Philosophers for satisfaction. But for reading upon Prodigies; or Commenting upon the Flight of Birds, or the Entrails of Beasts, These are things quite beside the Philosophers Business. If there be any thing you doubt of that falls under the Cognizance of Philosophy, I am ready to serve you in't; but your present Point being Augury, I shall take leave to acquaint you that a Servant I have at home, is as likely to make a right Judgment that way as any Man I know, I should not presume to name a Servant; Neither perchance would you think fit to make use of one, If the Necessity of your present Distress were not a very Competent and Reasonable Excuse.

51

Here's your Speech says *Aesop;* and your Credit saved whether They'll hear me or not. If they send for me, The Honour will be yours, in Case I deliver my self to their Liking, and the Disgrace will be mine then if I Miscarry. His Master was pleased beyond Measure with the Advice, but he did not as yet Understand whither it Tended.

Xanthus Presented himself early the next Morning before the Council, Where he Dilated upon the Matter according to his Instructions, and so referr'd them to his Servant for the Clearing of the Difficulty. The People with one Voice cry'd out *Where is he? Why does not he appear? Why has not his Master brought him along with him?* In short, *Aesop* was Immediately fetch'd into the Court, and at the very first sight of him, They All burst out a Laughing by Consent. This Fellow, says one, may have Skill perhaps in Divining, but he has nothing that's Humane about him. Another ask'd where he was Born, and whether or no Blocks had the Faculty of Speech in his Country. *Aesop,* upon This, Address'd himself to the Council.

You have here before ye, (says Aesop) an Ungracious Figure of a Man, which in truth is not a Subject for your Contempt, Nor is it a Reasonable Ground for your Despair, upon the Matter in Question. One Wise Man values another for his Understanding, not for his Beauty; Beside that the Deformity of my Person is no Incapacity at all as to your Business. Did you never tast Delicious Drink out of an ill-look'd Vessel? or did you never drink Wine that was Vapid, or Eager, out of a Vessel of Gold? 'Tis Sagacity and Strength of Reason that you have occasion for, not the force of Robust Limbs, nor the Delicacies of Colour and Proportion. Wherefore I must beseech you not to Judge of my Mind by my Body, nor to Condemn me Unheard. Upon this, they all cry'd out to him, If he had any thing to say for the Common Good, That he would speak it. *With your favour, says he, It is for that End I presume, that ye have called me hither, and it is with a great Zeal for your Service, that I stand now before ye: But when I consider the Weight of the matter in hand, and the Office that I am now to perform, it will as little stand with your Honours perhaps, to take the Opinion of a Slave into your Councils and Debates, as it will with my Condition to offer it; Beside the Risque I run of my Master's Displeasure upon the Event. But all this yet may be Obviated, my Fears secured, my Modesty Gratify'd, and your own Dignity Preserv'd, only by making me a Freeman before hand to qualify me for the Function.* They all said, it was a most Reasonable Thing, and presently Treated about the Price of his Liberty, and order'd the *Questors* to pay down the Money. When *Xanthus* saw that the thing must be done, He could not decently stand Higgling about the Price; But making a Virtue of Necessity, he chose rather to *Present Aesop* to the Common-wealth, than to *Sell* him. The *Samians* took it very kindly, And *Aesop* was presently *Manumiz'd* and made a Citizen in Form, Proclaim'd a Freeman; and after this Ceremony, he Discoursed upon the Subject of the Portent as follows.

I shall not need to tell so many Wise and Knowing Men, that the Eagle is a Royal Bird, and signifies a great King; that the Dropping of the Ring in the Bosom of a Slave that has no Power over himself, Portends the Loss of your Liberties if you do not look to your selves in Time; And that some Potent Prince has a Design upon ye. This put the *Samians* all a-fire to hear the Issue of the Prediction. In some short time after there came Ambassadors from *Croesus* the King of *Lydia*, to Demand a Tribute on the behalf of their Master, and Threat'ned the *Samians* with a War in the Case of a Refusal. This Affair came to be Debated in the Council, where the Majority was rather for Peace with Slavery, than for running the Risque of a Dispute; but they would not come to a Resolution yet, without first Consulting *Aesop* what they had best to do; Who gave them his Thought upon it in Words to this Effect.

Every Man in this World has Two Ways before him, That is to say,

First, *The Way of Liberty, that's Narrow and Rugged at the Entrance, but Plainer and Smoother still the further you go.* Secondly, *The Way of Servitude or Slavery, that seems to be Easie at first, but you'll find it afterwards to be full of Intolerable Difficulties.* The *Samians*, upon these Words, Declared themselves Unanimously for Liberty, and that since they were at present Free, They would never make Themselves Slaves by their own Consent: So the Ambassadors Departed, and there was a War Denounced.

When *Croesus* came to Understand the Resolution the *Samians* had taken, and how Inclinable they were to a Compliance, till *Aesop*, by the Power only of a few Words, Diverted them from it, he resolv'd to send for and Discourse with *Aesop*. So He made an Offer to the *Samians*, upon their sending *Aesop* to him, to put a Stop at present to the Course of his Arms. When *Aesop* came to hear of this Proposition, he told them, That he was not against their sending of him, Provided only, that he might tell them One Story before he Left them.

In Old Time, (says he) when some Beasts talked better Sence then many Men do now a days, there happen'd to be a fierce War betwixt the Wolves and the Sheep, And the Sheep, by the help of the Dogs, had rather the better on't. The Wolves, upon this, offer'd the Sheep a Peace, on Condition only that they might have their Dogs for Hostages; The Silly, Credulous Sheep agreed to't, and as soon as ever they had parted with the Dogs, The Wolves break in upon them, and Destroy them at Pleasure.

The *Samians* quickly smelt out the Moral of this Fable, and Cry'd out, One and All, that they would not part with *Aesop:* But this did not hinder *Aesop* however from putting himself Abord, and taking a Passage for *Lydia* with the Ambassadors.

Chapter fifteen: Aesop Presents himself before the King of Lydia

IMMEDIATELY Upon *Aesop's* Arrival in *Lydia*, he Presented himself before the King, who looking upon him with Contempt, Hatred, and Indignation; Is This a Man, says he, to hinder the King of *Lydia* from being Master of *Samos? Aesop* then with a Reverence after the *Lydian* Fashion, Deliver'd what he had to Say.

I am not here (says he, *Great King*) *in the Quality of a Man that's Given up by his Country, or under the Compulsion of any Force; but it is of my own Accord that I am now come to lay my self at your Majesty's Feet, and with this only Request, that you will vouchsafe me the Honour of your Royal Ear, and Patience but for a few Words.*

There was a Boy hunting of Locusts, and he had the Fortune to take a Grashopper. She found he was about to kill her, and Pleaded after this manner for her Life. Alas (says she) I never did any Body an Injury, and never had it either in my Will or my Power to do't. All my Business is my Song; and what will you be the better for my Death? The Youth's Heart relented, and he set the simple Grashopper at Liberty.

Your Majesty has now that Innocent Creature before you: There's nothing that I can pretend to but my Voice, which I have ever employ'd, so far as in me lay, to the Service of Mankind.

The King was so Tenderly moved with the Modesty and Prudence of the Man, That he did not only give him his Life, but bad him ask any thing farther that he had a Mind to, and it should be Granted him. Why then, says *Aesop*, (with that Veneration, Gratitude and Respect that the Case required) I do most humbly implore your Majesty's Favour for my Country-men the *Samians*. The King Granted him his Request, and Confirmed it under his Seal; Beside that the Piety of making that Petition his Choice, was a farther Recommendation of him to his Royal Kindness and Esteem.

Aesop, soon after this returned to *Samos* with the News of the Peace, where he was Welcomed with All the Instances of Joy and Thankfulness imaginable; Insomuch that they Erected a Statue for him, with an Inscription upon it, in Honour of his Memory. From *Samos* he return'd afterwards to *Croesus*, for whose sake he composed several of *Those Apologues* that pass in the World to this Day under his Name. His Fancy lay extremely to Travelling; but above All other Places he had the Greatest Mind to see *Babylon:* To which End he got Letters of Recommendation from *Croesus* to the King there: who, according to *Herodotus*, was a Friend and an Ally of *Croesus's* and his Name, *Labynetus*, not *Lycerus*, as *Planudes* had handed it down to us upon a Great Mistake. But his Curiosity led him first to pass through *Greece*, for the sake of the *Seven Wise Men*, whose Reputation was at That Time Famous All over the World. He had the Good Hap in his Travels to find them at *Corinth*, together with *Anacharsis*, and several of their Followers and Disciples, Where they were all Treated by *Periander* at a *Villa* of his not far from the Town. This Encounter was to the Common Satisfaction of the whole Company; the Entertainment Philosophical, and Agreeable, and among other Discourses, they had some Controversie upon the Subject of Government; and which was the most Excellent Form: *Aesop* being still for *Monarchy*, and the *Rest* for a *Common-wealth*. He Travell'd thence, a while after into *Asia*, and so to *Babylon*, according to his first Intention.

57

Chapter sixteen: Aesop Adopts Ennus. Ennus's Ingratitude and Falseness, and Aesop's Good Nature

IT was the Fashion in those Days for Princes to Exercise Tryals of Skill, in the Putting and Resolving of Riddles, and Intricate Questions; and He that was the Best at the Clearing or Untying of Knotty Difficulties carry'd the Prize. *Aesop's* Faculty lay notably that way, and Render'd him so Serviceable to the King, that it brought him both Reputation and Reward. It was his Unhappiness to have No Children, for the Comfort and Support of his Old Age; So that with the King's Consent, he Adopted a Young Man, who was Well Born, and Ingenious enough, but Poor; His Name was *Ennus*. *Aesop* took as much care of his Institution as if he had been his own Child, and Train'd him up in those Principles of Virtue and Knowledge that might most probably render him Great and Happy. But there's no working upon a Flagitious and Perverse Nature, by Kindness and Discipline, and 'tis Time Lost to think of Mastering so Incurable an Evil: So that *Ennus*, after the Manner of other Wicked Men, heaping one Villany upon another, Counterfeits his Fathers Name and Hand to certain Letters, where he Promises his Assistance to the Neighbour Princes against *Labynetus*. These Letters *Ennus* carries to the King, and Charges his Father with Treason, though in Appearance, with All the Trouble and Unwillingness that was possible, Only a Sense of his Duty to his King and his Country, swallow'd up All other Respects of Reverence and Modesty that a Son ows to a Father. The King took All these Calumnies for Instances of *Ennus*'s Affections to him, without the Least

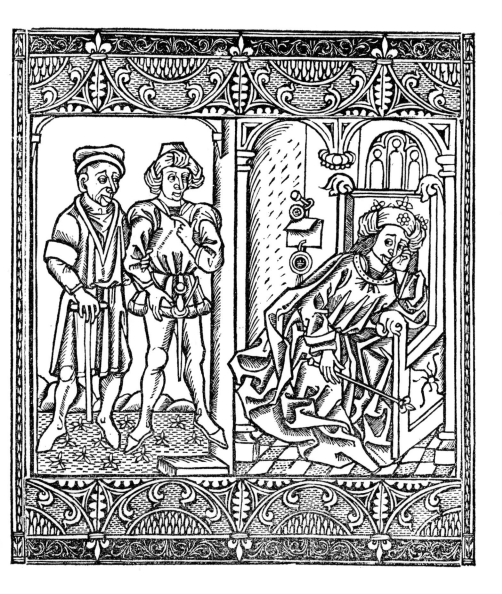

59

Suspicion of any Fraud in the Matter: So that without any further Enquiry, he Order'd *Aesop* to be put to Death. The Persons to whom the Care of his Execution was Committed, being well Assured of his Innocence, and of the King's Ungovernable Passions, took him out of the Way, and gave it out that he was Dead. Some few days after this, there came Letters to *Labynetus* from *Amasis* the King of *Aegypt*, wherein *Labynetus* was Desired by *Amasis* to send him a certain Architect that could Raise a Tower that should hang in the Air, and likewise Resolve All Questions. *Labynetus* was at a Great Loss what Answer to return, and the Fierceness of his Displeasure against *Aesop* being by This Time somewhat Abated, he began to Enquire after him with Great Passion, and would often Profess, that if the Parting with One half of his Kingdom could bring him to Life again, he would Give it. *Hermippus* and Others that had kept him out of the Way, told the King upon the Hearing of This, That *Aesop* was yet Alive; so they were Commanded to bring him forth; which they did, in All the Beastliness he had Contracted in the Prison. He did no sooner Appear, but he made his Innocence so Manifest, that *Labynetus* in Extreme Displeasure and Indignation, Commanded the False Accuser to be put to Death with most Exquisite Torments; but *Aesop*, after All this, Interceded for him, and Obtain'd his Pardon, upon a Charitable Presumption, that the Sence of so Great a Goodness and Obligation would yet Work upon him. *Herodotus* tells the Story of *Cambyses* the Son of *Cyrus*, and *Croesus*, and with what Joy *Cambyses* received *Croesus* again, after he was supposed to be put to Death by his Own Order; but then it Varies in This, that he Caused Those to be put to Death, that were to have seen the Execution done, for not Observing his Commands.

Chapter seventeen: Aesop's Letters of Morality to his Son Ennus

UPON *Aesop*'s coming again into Favour, he had the King of *Aegypt*'s Letter given him to Consider of, and Advised *Labynetus* to send him for Answer, That Early the next Spring he should have the satisfaction he desired. Things being in this state, *Aesop* took *Ennus* Home to him again, and so order'd the Matter, that he wanted neither Counsels nor Instructions, nor any other Helps or Lights that might Dispose him to the Leading of a Virtuous Life, as will Appear by the following Precepts.

My Son (says he) *Worship God with Care and Reverence, and with a Sincerity of Heart void of all Hypocrisy or Ostentation: Not as if that Divine Name and Power were only an Invention, to fright Women and Children, but know, That God is Omnipresent, True, and Almighty.*

Have a Care even of your Most Private Actions and Thoughts, for God sees thorough you, and your Conscience will bear Witness against you.

It is according to Prudence, as well as Nature, to pay that Honour to your Parents, that you expect your Children should pay to you.

Do all the Good you can to all Men, but in the first place to your Nearest Relations, and do no Hurt however, where you can do no Good.

Keep a Guard upon your Words as well as upon your Actions, that there be no Impurity in either.

Follow the Dictates of your Reason, and you are safe; and have a Care of Impotent Affections.

Apply your self to Learn more, so long as there's any thing Left that you do not know; and Value good Counsel before Money.

Our Minds must be Cultivated as well as our Plants; The Improvement of our Reason makes us like Angels, whereas the Neglect of it turns us into Beasts.

There's no Permanent and Inviolable Good, but Wisdom and Virtue, tho' the Study of it signifies Little without the Practice.

Do not think it impossible to be a Wise Man, without looking Sour upon it. Wisdom makes Men Severe, but not Inhumane.

It is Virtue not to be Vitious.

Keep Faith with all Men. Have a care of a Lye, as you would of Sacrilege. Great Bablers have no Regard either to Honesty or Truth.

Take Delight in, and frequent the Company of Good Men, for it will give you a Tincture of their Manners too.

Take heed of that Vulgar Error, of thinking that there is any Good in Evil. It is a Mistake when Men talk of Profitable Knavery, or of Starving Honesty; for Virtue and Justice carry all that is Good and Profitable along with them.

Let every Man mind his own Business, for Curiosity is Restless.

Speak Ill of no Body, and you are no more to hear Calumnies than to Report them: Beside that, they that Practice the One Commonly Love the Other.

Propose Honest Things, Follow Wholesome Counsels, and Leave the Event to God.

Let no Man Despair in Adversity, nor Presume in Prosperity, for all Things are Changeable.

Rise Early to your Business, Learn Good Things, and Oblige Good Men; These are Three Things you shall never Repent of.

Have a Care of Luxury and Gluttony; but of Drunkenness especially; for Wine as well as Age makes a Man a Child.

Watch for the Opportunities of doing things, for there's nothing well done but what's done in Season.

Love and Honour Kings, Princes, and Magistrates, for they are the Bands of Society, in Punishing of the Guilty, and Protecting the Innocent.

These, or such as these, were the Lessons that *Aesop* read daily to his Son; But so far was he from mending upon Them, that he grew every Day worse and worse, shewing that it is not in the Power of Art or Discipline to Rectify a Perverse Nature, or (as *Euripides* says) to *make a Man Wise that has no Soul*. But however, according to *Neveletus*, he came soon after to be Touched in Conscience for his Barbarous Ingratitude, and Died in a Raging Remorse for what he had done.

The Spring was now at Hand, and *Aesop* was preparing for the Task he had Undertaken About the Building of a Tower in the Air, and Resolving All Manner of Questions: But I shall say no more of that Romantick part of the History, than that he went into *Aegypt,* and Acquitted himself of his Commission to *Amasis* with great Reputation. From thence back again to *Labynetus,* Laden with Honours and Rewards; from whom he got Leave to Return into *Greece;* but upon Condition of Returning to *Babylon* by the First Opportunity.

Chapter eighteen: Aesop's Voyage to Delphos; his Barbarous Usage There, and his Death

WHEN *Aesop* had almost taken the whole Tour of *Greece*, he went to *Delphos*, either for the *Oracle's* sake, or for the sake of the *Wise Men* that Frequented that Place. But when he came thither, he found Matters to be quite otherwise then he expected, and so far from deserving the Reputation they had in the World for Piety and Wisdom, that he found them Proud, and Avaricious, and hereupon Deliver'd his Opinion of Them under this Fable.

I find (says he) *the Curiosity that brought me hither, to be much the Case of People at the Sea-side, that see something come Hulling toward them a great way off at Sea, and take it at first to be some Mighty Matter, but upon Driving nearer and nearer the Shore, it proves at last to be only a heap of Weeds and Rubbish.*

The Magistrates of the Place took Infinite Offence at this Liberty, and presently enter'd into a Conspiracy against him to take away his Life, for fear he should give them the same Character elsewhere in his Travels that he had done there upon the Place. It was not so safe, they thought, nor so Effectual a Revenge to make him away in private; but if they could so contrive it, as to bring him to a shameful End, under a Form of Justice, it would better answer their Business and Design. To which Purpose they caused a Golden Cup to be secretly convey'd into his Baggage, when he was Packing up to Depart. He was no sooner out of the Town upon his Journey, but immediately Pursu'd and taken upon the Way by the Officers, and Charg'd with *Sacrilege. Aesop* deny'd the Matter, and Laugh'd at them All for a Company of Mad Men; But upon the Searching of his Boxes, they took the Cup and shew'd it to the People, Hurrying him away to Prison in the Middle of his Defence. They brought him the Next Day into the Court, where notwithstanding the Proof of his Innocence, as clear as the Day, he was Condemned to Die; and his Sentence was to be thrown Headlong from a Rock, Down a Deep Precipice. After his Doom was Past, he Prevailed upon Them, with much ado to be heard a few Words, and so told them the Story of the Frog and the Mouse, as it stands in the Fable.*

This wrought nothing upon the Hearts of the *Delphians*, but as they were Bawling at the Executioner, to Dispatch and do his Office, *Aesop* on a sudden gave them the Slip, and Fled to an Altar hard by there, in hopes the Religion of the Place might have Protected him; but the *Delphians* told him that the Altars of the Gods were not to be any Sanctuary to those that Robbed their Temples; Whereupon he took Occasion to tell them the Fable of the *Eagle* and the *Beetle* to this following Effect.

A *Hare* that was hard put to't by an *Eagle*, took Sanctuary in a Ditch with a *Beetle*. The *Beetle* Interceded for the *Hare:* The *Eagle* Flapt off the former, and Devoured the other. The *Beetle* took this for an Affront to *Hospitality*, as well as to her Self, and so Meditated a Revenge, watch'd the *Eagle* up to her Nest, follow'd her, and took her Time, when the *Eagle* was Abroad, and so made a shift to Roll out the Eggs, and Destroy the Brood. The *Eagle* upon this Disappointment, Timber'd a

* See page 166.

great deal higher next Bout; The *Beetle* watch'd her still, and shew'd her the same Trick once again. Whereupon the *Eagle* made her Appeal to *Jupiter*, who gave her leave to lay her next Course of Eggs in his own Lap. But the *Beetle* found out a way to make *Jupiter* rise from his Throne; so that upon the Loosning of his Mantle, the Eggs fell from him at unawares, and the *Eagle* was a Third time Defeated. *Jupiter* stomach'd the Indignity, but upon hearing the Cause, he found the *Eagle* to be Aggressor, and so Acquitted the *Beetle*.

Now says *Aesop*, (after the telling of this Fable) you are not to Flatter your selves that the Prophaners of Holy Altars, and the Oppressors of the Innocent, shall ever escape Divine Vengeance. This Enraged the Magistrates to such a Degree, that they commanded the Officers immediately to take *Aesop* from the Altar, and Dispatch him away to his Execution. When *Aesop* found that neither the Holiness of the Place, nor the Clearness of his Innocence was sufficient to Protect him, and that he was to fall a Sacrifice to Subornation and Power, he gave them yet one Fable more as he was upon the Way to Execution.

There was an Old Fellow (says he) that had spent his whole Life in the Country without ever seeing the Town, he found himself Weak and Decaying, and nothing would serve, but his Friends must needs shew him the Town once before he Died. Their Asses were very well acquainted with the Way, and so they caused them to be made Ready, and turned the Old Man and Asses Loose, without a Guide, to try their Fortune, They were overtaken upon the Road by a Terrible Tempest, so that what with the Darkness, and the Violence of the Storm, the Asses were beaten out of their Way, and Tumbled with the Old Man into a Pit, where he had only time to Deliver his last Breath with this Exclamation. Miserable

Wretch that I am, to be Destroy'd, since Die I must, by the basest of Beasts; by Asses. And that's my Fate now in Suffering by the Hands of a Barbarous, Sottish People, that understand Nothing, either of Humanity or Honour: and Act contrary to the Tyes of Hospitality and Justice. But the Gods will not suffer my Blood to lie Unrevenged, and I doubt not but that in Time the Judgment of Heaven will give you to understand your Wickedness by your Punishment.

He was Speaking on, but they Pushed him Off Headlong from the Rock, and he was Dashed to Pieces with the Fall.

The *Delphians*, soon after This, were Visited with Famine and Pestilence, to such a Degree that they went to Consult the Oracle of *Apollo* to know what Wickedness it was had brought these Calamities upon Them. The Oracle gave them this Answer, That they were to Expiate for the Death of *Aesop*. In the Conscience of their Barbarity, they Erected a *Pyramid* to his Honour, and it is upon Tradition, that a great many of the Most Eminent Men among the *Greeks* of that Season, went afterwards to *Delphos* upon the News of the Tragical End of *Aesop*, to Learn the Truth of the History, and found upon Enquiry, That the Principal of the Conspirators had laid Violent Hands upon themselves.

The Fables of Aesop

Jupiter and a Herds-Man

A *Herds-man* that had lost a Calf out of his Grounds, sent up and down after it; and when he could get No Tydings on't, he betook himself at last to his Prayers, according to the Custom of the World, when People are brought to a Forc'd-Put. Great *Jupiter* (says he) Do but shew me the *Thief* that stole my Calf, and I'll give thee a *Kid* for a Sacrifice. The Word was no sooner pass'd but the *Thief* appear'd; which was indeed a *Lyon*. This Discovery put him to his Prayers once again. I have not forgotten my Vow, says he, but now thou hast brought me to the *Thief*, I'll make that *Kid* a *Bull*, if thou'lt but set me Quit of him again.

THE MORAL *We cannot be too Careful, and Considerate what Vows and Promises we make; for the very Granting of our Prayers turns many times to our Utter Ruine.*

A Dog and a Wolfe

THERE was a Hagged Carrion of a *Wolfe*, and a jolly sort of a Gentile *Dog*, with good Flesh upon's Back, that fell into Company together upon the King's Highway. The *Wolfe* was wonderfully pleas'd with his Companion, and as Inquisitive to Learn how he brought himself to That Blessed State of Body. Why, says the *Dog*, I keep my Master's House from Thieves, and I have very Good Meat, Drink, and Lodging for my pains. Now if you'll go along with Me, and do as I do, you may fare as I fare. The *Wolfe* Struck up the Bargain, and so away they Trotted together: But as they were Jogging on, the *Wolfe* spy'd a Bare Place about the *Dog's* Neck, where the Hair was worn off. Brother (says he) how comes this I prethee? Oh, That's Nothing, says the *Dog*, but the Fretting of my *Collar* a little. Nay, says T'other, if there be a *Collar* in the Case, I know Better Things then to sell my Liberty for a Crust.

THE MORAL *We are so Dazzel'd with the Glare of a Splendid Appearance, that we can hardly Discern the Inconveniences that Attend it. 'Tis a Comfort to have Good Meat and Drink at Command, and Warm Lodging: But He that sells his Freedom, for the Cramming of his Gutt, has but a Hard Bargain of it.*

An Ax and a Forrest

A Carpenter that had got the Iron-Work of an *Ax* already, went to the Next *Forrest* to beg only so much Wood as would make a Handle to't. The Matter seem'd so small, that the Request was Easily Granted; but when the Timber-Trees came to find that the Whole Wood was to be Cut down by the Help of this Handle; *There's No Remedy*, they cry'd, *but Patience, when People are undone by their own Folly*.

THE MORAL *Nothing goes nearer a Man in his Misfortunes, than to find himself Undone by his Own Folly, or but any way Accessary to his own Ruin.*

A Fox that lost his Tail

THERE was a *Fox* taken in a Trap, that was glad to Compound for his Neck by leaving his *Tail* behind him. It was so Uncouth a Sight, for a *Fox* to appear without a *Tail*, that the very Thought on't made him e'en Weary of his Life; for 'twas a Loss never to be Repair'd: But however for the Better Countenance of the Scandal, he got *the Master and Wardens of the Foxes Company* to call a *Court of Assistants*, where he himself appear'd and made a Learned Discourse upon the Trouble, the Uselessness, and the Indecency of *Foxes* Wearing *Tails*. He had no sooner say'd out his Say, but up rises a Cunning Snap, then at the Board, who desir'd to be Inform'd, whether the Worthy Member that Mov'd against the Wearing of *Tails*, gave his Advice for the Advantage of Those that *Had Tails*, or to Palliate the Deformity and Disgrace of Those that had *None*.

THE MORAL *When a Man has any Notable Defect, or Infirmity about him, whether by Nature, or by Chance, 'tis the Best of his Play, to try the Humour, if he turn it into a Fashion.*

A Fox and Grapes

THERE was a Time, when a *Fox* would have Ventur'd as far for a Bunch of *Grapes*, as for a Shoulder of *Mutton*, and it was a *Fox* of Those days, and That Palate, that stood Gaping under a Vine, and licking his Lips at a most Delicious Cluster of Grapes that he had Spy'd out there; He fetch'd a Hundred and a Hundred Leaps at it, till as last, when he was as Weary as a Dog, and found that there was No Good to be done; *Hang 'em* (says He) *they are as Sour as Crabs;* and so away he went, turning off the Disappointment with a Jest.

THE MORAL *'Tis a Matter of Skill and Address, when a Man cannot Honestly Compass what he would be at, to Appear Easy and Indifferent upon All Repulses and Disappointments.*

The Stag and the Oxen

A *Stag* that was hard set by the Huntsmen, betook himself to a Stall for Sanctuary, and prevail'd with the *Oxen* to Conceal him the Best they could; so they cover'd him with Straw, and by and by in comes the Keeper to Dress the Cattle, and to Feed them; and when he had done his Work he went his Way without any Discovery. The *Stag* reckon'd himself by This Time to be out of all Danger; but one of the *Oxen* that had more Brains then his Fellows, advis'd him not to be too Confident neither; for the Servant, says he, is a Puzling Fool, that heeds Nothing; but when my Master comes, he'll have an Eye *Here and There and Every where*, and will most certainly find ye out. Upon the very Speaking of the Word, in comes the Master, and He spies out Twenty Faults, I warrant ye; This was not Well, and That was not Well; till at last, as he was Prying and Groping up and down, he felt the Horns of the *Stag* under the Straw, and so made Prize of him.

THE MORAL *He that would be sure to have his Business Well Done, must either Do it Himself, or see the Doing of it; Beside that many a Good Servant is Spoil'd by a Careless Master.*

An Ape and a Fox

AN *Ape* that found Many Inconveniences by going *Bare-Arse*, went to a *Fox* that had a Well-spread, Bushy *Tayle*, and begg'd of him only a little piece on't to Cover his Nakedness: For (says he) you have enough for Both, and what needs more then you have Occasion for? Well, *John* (says the *Fox*) be it More, or be it Less, you get not one single Hair on't; for I would have ye know, Sirrah, that the *Tayle* of a *Fox* was never made for the Buttocks of an *Ape*.

THE MORAL *Providence has Assign'd Every Creature its Station, Lot, Make and Figure; and 'tis not for Us to stand Correcting the Works of an Incomprehensible Wisdom, and an Almighty Power.*

83

A League betwixt the Wolves and the Sheep

THERE was a time when the *Sheep* were so Hardy as to Wage War with the *Wolves;* and so long as they had the *Dogs* for their Allies, they were upon all Encounters, at least a Match for their Enemies. Upon this Consideration, the *Wolves* sent their Embassadors to the *Sheep*, to Treat about a Peace, and in the mean Time there were Hostages given on both Sides; the *Dogs* on the part of the *Sheep*, and the *Wolves Whelps* on the Other Part, till Matters might be brought to an Issue. While they were upon Treaty, the *Whelps* fell a Howling; The *Wolves* cryed out Treason; and pretending an Infraction in the Abuse of their Hostages, fell upon the *Sheep* immediately without their *Dogs*, and made them pay for the Improvidence of leaving themselves without a Guard.

THE MORAL *'Tis senseless in the Highest Degree to think of Establishing an Alliance among those that Nature her self has Divided, by an Inconciliable Disagreement. Beside, that a Foolish Peace is much more Destructive then a Bloody War.*

85

A Camel Praying for Horns

It stuck filthily in the *Camel's* Stomach, that *Bulls, Stags, Lions, Bears,* and the like, should be Armed with *Horns, Teeth,* and *Claws,* and that a Creature of his Size should be left Naked and Defenceless. Upon This Thought he fell down upon his Marrow-bones, and begg'd of *Jupiter* to give him a Pair of Horns, but the Request was so Ridiculous, that *Jupiter,* instead of *Horning* him, Order'd Him to be Cropt, and so Punish'd Him with the loss of his Ears, which Nature had Allow'd him, for being so Unreasonable as to ask for *Horns,* that Providence never intended him.

The Moral *The Bounties of Heaven are in such manner Distributed, that Every Living Creature has its Share; beside, that to Desire Things against Nature, is Effectually to Blame the very Author of Nature it self.*

A Doctor and his Patient

PRAY *Sir, How d'ye Find your self?* says the *Dr.* to his *Patient.* Why truly, says the *Patient;* I have had a Violent Sweat; *Oh the best Sign in the World* quoth the *Dr.* And then a little while after he is at it again, with a *Pray How d'ye find your Body?* Alas says the T'other, I have just now such a Terrible Fit of Horror and Shaking upon me! *Why this is all as it should be,* says the *Physician,* It shews a Mighty Strength of Nature. And then he comes over him a Third time with the same Question again; Why I am all swell'd, says T'other, as if I had a Dropsy; *Best of All* quoth the *Doctor,* and goes his Way. Soon after This, comes one of the Sick Man's Friends to him with the same Question, how he felt himself; why truly so Well, says he, that I am e'en ready to Dye, of I know not how many Good Signs and Tokens.

THE MORAL *A Death-Bed Flattery is the worst of Treacheries.*

A Snake and a File

THERE was a *Snake* got into a Smith's Shop, and fell to Licking of a *File;* She Saw the *File Bloody*, and still the Bloodier it was, the more Eagerly she Lick'd it, upon a Foolish Fancy, that it was the *File* that Bled, and that She her self had the Better on't. In the Conclusion, when she could Lick no Longer, she fell to Biting; but finding at last she could do no more Good upon't with her Teeth then with her Tongue, she Fairly left it.

THE MORAL *'Tis a Madness to stand Biting and Snapping at any thing to no manner of purpose, more then the Gratifying of an Impotent Rage, in the fancy of Hurting Another, when in Truth, we only Wound our selves.*

89

A Wolf and a Fox

A *Wolf* that had a mind to take his Ease, Stor'd himself Privately with Provisions, and so kept Close a while. Why, how now Friend says a *Fox* to him, we han't seen you abroad at the Chase this many a Day! Why truly says the *Wolf*, I have gotten an Indisposition that keeps me much at Home, and I hope I shall have Your Prayers for my Recovery. The *Fox* had a Fetch in't, and when he saw it would not Fadge, Away goes he presently to a Shepherd, and tells him where he might surprise a *Wolf* if he had a mind to't. The Shepherd follow'd his Directions, and Destroy'd him. The *Fox* immediately, as his Next Heir, repairs to his Cell, and takes Possession of his Stores; but he had little Joy of the Purchase, for in a very short time, the same Shepherd did as much for the *Fox*, as he had done before for the *Wolf*.

THE MORAL *'Tis with Sharpers as 'tis with Pikes, they Prey upon their own kind; And 'tis a Pleasant Scene enough, when Thieves fall out among themselves, to see the Cutting of One Diamond with Another.*

A Stag Drinking

As a *Stag* was Drinking upon the Bank of a Clear Stream, he saw his Image in the Water, and Enter'd upon This Contemplation upon't. Well! says he, if these Pitiful Shanks of mine were but Answerable to this Branching Head, I can but think how I should Defy all my Enemies. The Words were hardly out of his Mouth, but he Discover'd a Pack of Dogs coming full Cry towards him. Away he Scours cross the Fields, Casts off the Dogs, and Gains a Wood; but Pressing through a Thicket, the Bushes held him by the Horns, till the Hounds came in and Pluck'd him down. The last thing he said was this. What an Unhappy Fool was I, to take my Friends for my Enemies, and my Enemies for my Friends! I Trusted to my *Head*, that has Betray'd me, and I found fault with my *Legs*, that would otherwise have brought me off.

THE MORAL *He that does not thoroughly know himself, may be well allowed to make a False Judgment upon other Matters that most Nearly concern him.*

93

Asses to Jupiter

THE *Asses* found themselves once so Intolerably Oppressed with Cruel Masters, and Heavy Burdens, that they sent their Ambassadors to *Jupiter*, with a Petition for Redress. *Jupiter* found the Request Unreasonable, and so gave them this Answer, That Humane Society could not be preserved without Carrying Burdens some way or other: So that if they would but Joyn, and Piss up a River, that the Burdens which they now Carry'd by Land might be Carried by Water, they should be Eas'd of that Grievance. This set them all a Pissing Immediately, and the Humour is kept up to this very Day, that whenever *One Ass* Pisses, the rest Piss for Company.

THE MORAL *'Tis the uttermost Degree of Madness and Folly, to appeal from Providence and Nature.*

A Hen and a Swallow

THERE was a Foolish *Hen* that sat Brooding upon a Nest of *Snakes Eggs.* A *Swallow* that Observ'd it, went and told her the Danger on't. Little do you think, says she, what you at this Instant are a Doing, and that You are just now Hatching your Own Destruction; for This Good Office will be your Ruine.

THE MORAL *'Tis the Hard Fortune of many a Good Natur'd Man to* breed up a Bird to Pick out his own Eyes, *in despite of All Cautions to the Contrary.*

A Bat, Birds, and Beasts

UPON a Desperate and a Double Battel betwixt the *Birds* and the *Beasts*, the *Bat* stood *Neuter*, till she found that the *Beasts* had the Better on't, and then went over to the stronger Side. But it came to pass afterward (as the Chance of War is Various) that the *Birds* Rally'd their Broken Troops, and carry'd the Day; and away she went Then to T'other Party, where she was Try'd by a Council of War as a Deserter; Stript, Banish'd, and finally Condemn'd never to see Day-light again.

THE MORAL Trimming, *in some Cases, is Foul, and Dishonest; in others Laudable, and in some again, not only Honest, but Necessary. The Nicety lies in the skill of Distinguishing upon Cases, Times, and Degrees.*

A Horse and an Ass

IN the Days of Old, when *Horses* spoke *Greek* and *Latin*, and *Asses* made *Syllogisms*, there happen'd an Encounter upon the Road, betwixt a Proud Pamper'd *Jade* in the Full Course of his Carriere, and a Poor Creeping *Ass*, under a Heavy Burden, that had Chopt into the same Track with him. Why, how now Sirrah, says he, D'ye not see by these Arms, and Trappings, to what Master I belong? And D'ye not Understand that when I have That Master of mine upon my Back, the Whole Weight of the State rests upon My Shoulders? Out of the way thou slavish Insolent Animal, or I'll Tread thee to Dirt. The Wretched *Ass* immediately Slunk aside, with this Envious Reflection betwixt his Teeth, [*What would I give to Change Conditions with that Happy Creature there.*] This Fancy would not out of the Head of him, 'till it was his Hap some Few Days after to see This very *Horse* doing Drudgery in a Common Dung-Cart. Why how now Friend (says the *Ass*) How comes This about? Only the Chance of the War, says the Other: I was a *Soldier's Horse*, you must know; and my Master carry'd me into a Battel, where I was Shot, Hack'd, and Maim'd; and you have here before Your Eyes the Catastrophe of My Fortune.

THE MORAL *The Folly, and the Fate, of Pride and Arrogance. The Mistake of Placing Happiness in any thing that may be taken away, and the Blessing of Freedom in a Mean Estate.*

A Horse and a Lion

THERE was an Old Hungry *Lion* would fain have been Dealing with a piece of Good *Horse-Flesh* that he had in his Eye; but the *Nag* he thought would be too Fleet for him, unless he could supply the want of Heels, by Artifice, and Address. He puts himself into the Garb, and Habit of a Professor of Physick, and according to the Humor of the World, sets up for a Doctor of the College. Under this Pretext, he lets fall a Word or two by way of Discourse, upon the Subject of his Trade; but the *Horse* Smelt him out, and presently a Crotchet came in his Head how he might Countermine him. I got a Thorn in my Foot T'other day, says the *Horse*, as I was Crossing a Thicket, and I am e'en quite Lame on't. Oh, says the New Physician, Do but hold up your Leg a little, and I'll Cure ye immediately. The *Lion* presently puts himself in posture for the Office; but the Patient was too Nimble for his Doctor, and so soon as ever he had him Fair for his Purpose, gave him so Terrible a Rebuke upon the Forehead with his Heel, that he laid him at his Length, and so got off with a whole Skin, before the Other could Execute his Design.

THE MORAL Harm Watch, Harm Catch, *is but according to the Common Rule of Equity and Retaliation, and a very Warrantable Way of Deceiving the Deceiver.*

A Frog and an Oxe

As a Huge Over-grown *Oxe* was Grazing in a Meadow, an Old Envious *Frog* that stood Gaping at him hard by, call'd out to her Little Ones, to take Notice of the Bulk of That Monstrous Beast; and see, says she, if I don't make my self now the Bigger of the Two. So she Strain'd Once, and Twice, and went still Swelling on and on, till in the Conclusion she Forc'd her self, and Burst.

THE MORAL *Betwixt Pride, Envy, and Ambition, men Fancy Themselves to be Bigger than they are, and Other People to be Less: And This Tumor Swells it self at last till it makes All Fly.*

An Ant and a Fly

THERE happen'd a Warm Dispute betwixt an *Ant* and a *Fly*. Why, Where's the Honour, or the Pleasure in the World, says the *Fly*, that I have not My Part in? Are not All Temples and Palaces open to me? Am not I the Taster to Gods and Princes in All their Sacrifices and Entertainments? Am I not serv'd in Gold and Silver? And is not my Meat and Drink still of the Best? And all This, without either Money or Pains? I trample upon Crowns, and Kiss what Ladies Lips I please. And what have you now to pretend to all this While? Why, says the *Ant*, You Value Your self upon the Access You have to the Altars of the Gods, the Cabinets of Princes, and to All Publick Feasts and Collations: And what's all This but the Access of an Intruder, not of a Guest; For People are so far from Liking Your Company, that they Kill ye as fast as they can Catch ye. You are a Plague to 'em Wherever You come. Your very Breath has Maggot's in't, and for the Kiss you Brag of, what is it but the Perfume of the last Dunghil you Touch'd upon, once Remov'd; For My Part, I live upon what's my Own, and Work Honestly in the Summer to Maintain my self in the Winter; Whereas the whole Course of Your Scandalous Life is only Cheating or Sharping, one Half of the Year, and Starving the Other.

THE MORAL *Here's an Emblem of Industry, and Luxury, set forth at large; with the Sober Advantages, and the Scandalous Excesses of the One and of the Other.*

105

A Fox and a Carv'd Head

As a *Fox* was rumidging among a great many *Carv'd Figures*, there was One very Extraordinary Piece among the Rest. He took it up, and when he had Consider'd it a while; Well, (says he) What Pity 'tis, that so Exquisite an Outside of a Head should not have one Grain of Sense in't.

THE MORAL *'Tis not the Barber or the Taylor that makes the Man: and 'tis No New Thing to see a Fine Wrought Head without so much as One Grain of Salt in't.*

Thieves that Stole a Cock

A Band of *Thieves* Brake into a House once, and found Nothing in't to Carry away, but One Poor *Cock*. The *Cock* said as much for Himself as a *Cock* could say; but Insisted Chiefly upon the Services of his Calling People up to their Work, when 'twas time to Rise. Sirrah (says one of the *Thieves*) You had better have let That Argument Alone; for Your Waking the Family Spoils our Trade, and We are to be Hang'd forsooth for your Bawling.

THE MORAL *That which is One Body's Meat, is Another Body's Poyson; as the Trussing up of Thieves is the Security of Honest Men. One Foolish Word is enough to Spoil a Good Cause, and 'tis many a Man's Fortune to Cut his Own Throat with his Own Arguments.*

A Crow and a Raven

YOUR *Raven* has a Reputation in the World for a Bird of Omen, and a kind of small *Prophet*. A *Crow* that had Observ'd the *Raven's* Manner and Way of Delivering his Predictions, sets up for a *Foreboder* too; and so gets upon a Tree, and there stands Nodding and Croaking, just over the Heads of some People that were Passing by. They were a little Surpriz'd at first; but so soon as they saw how 'twas. Come, my Masters (says One of the Company) let's e'en go forward, for this is but the Chattering of a Foolish *Crow*, and it signifies Nothing.

THE MORAL *How are Superstitious Men Hagg'd out of their Wits and Senses, with the Fancy of Omens, Forebodings, Old Wives Tales and Visions; and upon a Final Examination of the Matter, Nothing at all in the Bottom on't!*

A Fox and a Stork

THERE was a Great Friendship once betwixt a *Fox* and a *Stork*, and the Former would needs Invite the Other to a Treat. They had Several Soups serv'd up in Broad Dishes and Plates, and so the *Fox* fell to Lapping himself, and bad his Guest Heartily Welcom to what was before him. The *Stork* found he was Put upon, but set so good a Face however upon his Entertainment; that his Friend by All means must take a Supper with Him That night in Revenge. The *Fox* made Several Excuses upon the Matter of Trouble and Expence, but the *Stork* in fine, would not be said Nay, So that at last, he promis'd him to come. The Collation was serv'd up in Glasses, with Long Narrow Necks, and the Best of Every thing that was to be had. Come (says the *Stork* to his Friend) Pray be as Free as if you were at home, and so fell to't very Savourly Himself. The *Fox* quickly found This to be a Trick, though he could not but Allow of the Contrivance as well as the Justice of the Revenge. For such a Glass of Sweet-Meats to the One, was just as much to the Purpose, as a Plate of Porridge to the Other.

THE MORAL *'Tis allowable in all the Liberties of Conversation to give a Man a* Rowland for his Oliver, *and to pay* him in his Own Coin, *as we say; provided always that we keep within the Compass of Honour, and Good Manners.*

III

A Countryman and a Snake

THERE was a *Snake* that Bedded himself under the Threshold of a Country-House: A *Child* of the Family happen'd to set his Foot upon't; The *Snake* bit him, and he Dy'd on't. The *Father* of the *Child* made a Blow at the *Snake*, but Miss'd his Aim, and only left a Mark behind him upon the Stone where he Struck. The *Countryman* Offer'd the *Snake*, some time after This, to be Friends again. No, says the *Snake*, so long as you have This Flaw upon the Stone in Your Eye, and the Death of the *Child* in your Thought, there's No Trusting of ye.

THE MORAL *In Matters of Friendship and Trust, we can never be too Tender; but yet there's a Great Difference betwixt Charity and Facility. We may Hope Well in many Cases, but let it be without Venturing Neck, and All upon't,* for New-Converts *are Slippery.*

A Dog, a Sheep and a Wolf

A *Dog* brought an Action of the Case against a *Sheep*, for some Certain Measures of Wheat, that he had lent him. The Plaintiff prov'd the Debt by Three Positive Witnesses, The *Wolf*, the *Kite*, and the *Vultur*. (*Testes Probi & Legales*) The *Defendant* was cast in *Costs and Damages*, and forc'd to sell the Wool off his Back to Satisfie the Creditor.

THE MORAL *'Tis not a Straw matter whether the Main Cause be Right or Wrong, or the Charge True or False; Where the Bench, Jury and Witnesses are in a Conspiracy against the Pris'ner.*

A Wolf, Kid and Goat

A *Goat* that was going out one Morning for a Mouthful of Fresh Grass, Charg'd her *Kid* upon her Blessing, not to Open the Door till she came back, to any Creature that had not a Beard. The *Goat* was no sooner out of sight, but up comes a *Wolf* to the Door, that had Over-heard the Charge; and in a Small Pipe calls to the *Kid* to let her *Mother* come in. The *Kid* smelt out the Roguery, and bad the *Wolf* shew his *Beard*, and the Door should be Open to him.

THE MORAL *There never was any Hypocrite so Disguis'd but he had some Mark or Other yet to be known by.*

An Ape and a Dolphin

PEOPLE were us'd in the Days of Old, to carry Gamesome *Puppies* and *Apes* with 'em to Sea, to pass away the Time withal. Now there was One of these *Apes*, it seems, aboard a Vessel that was cast away in a very great Storm. As the Men were Paddling for their Lives, and an *Ape* for Company, a certain *Dolphin* that took him for a Man, got him upon his Back, and was making towards Land with him. He had him into a Safe Road call'd the *Pryaus*, and took occasion to ask the *Ape* whether he was an *Athenian* or not? He told him Yes, and of a very Ancient Family there. Why then (says the *Dolphin*) You know *Pyraus*: Oh! exceedingly well says T'other. (taking it for the Name of a Man) Why *Pyraus* is my very very Particular Good Friend. The *Dolphin* upon This, had such an Indignation for the Impudence of the *Buffon-Ape*, that he gave him the Slip from between his Legs, and there was an end of my very Good Friend, the *Athenian*.

THE MORAL *Bragging, Lying, and Pretending, has Cost many a Man his Life and Estate.*

A Musician

A Man that had a very Course Voice, but an Excellet *Musique-Room*, would be still Practising in that Chamber, for the Advantage of the *Eccho*. He took such a Conceit upon't, that he must needs be shewing his Parts upon a Publick Theatre, where he Perform'd so very Ill, that the Auditory Hiss'd him off the Stage, and threw Stones at him.

THE MORAL *A Man may Like himself very Well in his Own Glass, and yet the World not Fall in Love with him in Publick. But the Truth on't is, we are Partial in our own Case, and there's no Reading of our Selves but with Other Men's Eyes.*

The Hares and the Frogs

ONCE upon a time the *Hares* found themselves mightily Unsatisfy'd with a Miserable Condition they Liv'd in, and call'd a Council to Advise upon't. Here we live, says one of 'em, at the Mercy of Men, Dogs, Eagles, and I know not how many Other Creatures and Vermin, that Prey upon us at Pleasure; Perpetually in Frights, Perpetually in Danger; And therefore I am absolutely of Opinion that we had better Die once for All, then live at This rate in a Continual Dread that's Worse then Death it self. The Motion was Seconded and Debated, and a Resolution Immediately taken, *One and All*, to Drown Themselves. The Vote was no sooner Pass'd, but away they Scudded with That Determination to the next Lake. Upon this Hurry, there leapt a Whole Shoal of *Frogs* from the Bank into the Water, for fear of the *Hares*. Nay, then my Masters, says one of the Gravest of the Company, pray let's have a little Patience. Our Condition I find is not altogether so bad as we fancy'd it; for there are those you see that are as much afraid of Us, as we are of Others.

THE MORAL *There's No Contending with the Orders and Decrees of Providence. He that Made us knows what's Fittest for us; and Every Man's Own Lot, (well Understood and Manag'd) is Undoubtedly the Best.*

An Old Dog and his Master

AN *Old Dog*, that in his Youth had led his *Master* many a Merry Chase, and done him all the Offices of a Trusty Servant, came at last, upon falling from his Speed and Vigor, to be Loaden at every turn with Blows and Reproaches for it. Why Sir, (says the *Dog*) My Will is as Good as ever it was; but my Strength and my Teeth are gone; and you might with as good a Grace, and Every jot as much Justice, Hang me up because I'm *Old*, as Beat me because I'm *Impotent*.

THE MORAL *The Reward of Affection and Fidelity must be the Work of another World: Not but that the Conscience of Well Doing is a Comfort that may pass for a Recompence even in This; in Despite of Ingratitude and Injustice.*

123

A Mountain in Labour

WHEN *Mountains* cry out, people may well be Excus'd the Apprehension of some Prodigious Birth. This was the Case here in the Fable. The Neighbourhood were All at their Wits end, to consider what would be the Issue of That Labour, and instead of the Dreadful Monster that they Expected, Out comes at last a Ridiculous *Mouse*.

THE MORAL *Much ado about Nothing.*

125

A Man and Two Wives

It was now *Cuckow-Time*, and a Certain *Middle-Ag'd Man*, that was Half-Gray, Half-Brown, took a fancy to Marry Two Wives, of an Age One under Another, and Happy was the Woman that could please him Best. They took Mighty Care of him to All manner of Purposes, and still as they were Combing the Good Man's Head, they'd be Picking out here and there a Hair to make it all of a Colour. The Matronly Wife, she Pluck'd out All the *Brown* Hairs, and the Younger the *White:* So that they left the Man in the Conclusion no better than a *Bald Buzzard* betwixt them.

The Moral *'Tis a much Harder Thing to Please Two Wives than Two Masters; and He's a Bold Man that offers at it.*

Two Frogs that wanted Water

UPON the Drying of a *Lake*, *Two Frogs* were forc'd to Quit, and to seek for Water elsewhere, As they were upon the Search, they Discover'd a very deep Well. Come, (says One to T'other) Let us e'en go down here, without Looking any further. You say well, says her Companion; but what if the Water should fail us Here too? How shall we get Out again.

THE MORAL *'Tis Good Advice to Look before we Leap.*

A Wolf and a Sow

A Wolf came to a Sow that was just lying down, and very kindly offer'd to take care of her Litter. The Sow as Civilly thank'd her for her Love, and desir'd she would be pleas'd to stand off a little, and do her the Good Office at a Distance.

THE MORAL *There are no Snares so Dangerous as those that are laid for us under the Name of Good Offices.*

I

A Dog and a Thief

As a Gang of *Thieves* were at work to Rob a House, a *Mastiff* took the Alarum, and fell a Baying. One of the Company spoke him fair, and would have Stopt his Mouth with a Crust: No, says the *Dog*, This will not do, for Several Reasons. First, I'll take no Bribes to Betray my Master. Secondly, I am not such a Fool neither, as to sell the Ease and Liberty of my Whole Life to come, for a piece of Bread in Hand: For when you have Rifled my Master; pray who shall Maintain Me?

THE MORAL *Fair Words, Presents, and Flatteries, are the Methods of Treachery in Courts, as well as in Cottages, only the Dogs are Truer to their Masters than the Men.*

131

The Kite, Hawk, and Pigeons

THE *Pigeons* finding themselves Persecuted by the *Kite,* made Choice of the *Hawk* for their Guardian. The *Hawk* sets up for their Protector; but under Countenance of That Authority, makes more Havock in the *Dove-House* in Two Days, than the *Kite* could have done in Twice as many Months.

THE MORAL *'Tis a Dangerous Thing for People to call in a Powerful and Ambitious man for their Protector: and upon the Clamour of here and there a Private person, to hazard the Whole Community.*

133

Large Promises

THERE was a Poor Sick Man, that according to the Course of the World, when Physicians had given him over, betook himself to his Prayers, and Vow'd a Sacrifice of a Thousand Oxen ready down upon the Nail, to either *Apollo*, or *Aesculapius*, which of the Two would deliver him from This Disease. Ah my Dear (says his Wife) Have a care what You Promise; for where would you have These Oxen if you should Recover? Sweet Heart (says he) thou talk'st like a Fool. Have the Gods Nothing else to do, dost think, than to leave their Bus'ness, and come down to sue me in an Action of Debt? They Restor'd him however for that Bout, to make Tryal of his Honesty and Good Faith. He was no sooner up, but for want of Living Oxen, he made out his Number upon Paste, and Offer'd them up in Form upon an Altar. For this Mockery, Divine Vengeance pursu'd him, and he had an Apparition came to him in a Dream, that bad him go and Search in such a Place near the Coast, and he should find a Considerable Treasure: Away he went, and as he was looking for the Money fell into the Hands of Pyrates. He begg'd hard for his Liberty, and Offer'd a Thousand Talents of Gold for his Ransome; but they would not Trust him, and so he was carried away, and sold afterwards as a Slave for as many Groats.

THE MORAL *The Dev'll was Sick, the Dev'll a Monk would be; The Dev'll was Well, the Dev'll a Monk was He.*

A Hare and a Tortoise

WHAT a Dull Heavy Creature (says a *Hare*) is This same *Tortoise!* And yet (says the *Tortoise*) I'll run with you for a Wager. 'Twas *Done and Done*, and the *Fox*, by Consent, was to be the Judge. They started together, and the *Tortoise* kept jogging on still till he came to the End of the Course. The *Hare* lay'd himself down about Midway, and took a Nap; for, says he, I can fetch up the *Tortoise* when I please: But he Over-slept himself it seems, for when he came to wake, though he scudded away as fast as 'twas possible, the *Tortoise* got to the Post before him, and Won the Wager.

THE MORAL Up and be Doing, *is an Edifying Text; for Action is the Bus'ness of Life, and there's no Thought of ever coming to the End of our Journey in time, if we Sleep by the Way.*

A Swallow and other Birds

THERE was a Country Fellow at work a Sowing his Grounds, and a *Swallow* (being a Bird famous for Providence and Foresight) call'd a company of *Little Birds* about her, and bad 'em take Good Notice what that Fellow was a doing. You must know (says the *Swallow*) that all the Fowlers Nets and Snares are made of *Hemp*, or *Flax*; and that's the Seed that he is now a Sowing. Pick it up in time for fear of what may come on't. In short, they put it off, till it took Root; and then again, till it was sprung up into the Blade. Upon this, the *Swallow* told 'em once for All, that it was not yet too Late to prevent the Mischief, if they would but bestir themselves, and set Heartily about it; but finding that no heed was given to what she said; She e'en bad adieu to her old Companions in the Woods, and so betook her self to a City Life, and to the Conversation of Men. This *Flax* and *Hemp* came in time to be gather'd, and Wrought, and it was this *Swallow's* Fortune to see Several of the very same *Birds* that she had forewarn'd, taken in Nets, made of the very Stuff she told them of. They came at last to be Sensible of the folly of slipping their Opportunity; but they were Lost beyond All Redemption first.

THE MORAL *Wise Men read Effects in their Causes, but Fools will not Believe them till 'tis too late to prevent the Mischief. Delay in these Cases is Mortal.*

137

A Sick Kite and her Mother

PRAY *Mother* (says a Sick *Kite*) Give over these Idle *Lamentations*, and let me rather have your Prayers. Alas! my Child, (says the Dam) which of the Gods shall I go to, for a Wretch that has Robb'd All their Altars?

THE MORAL *Nothing but the Conscience of a Virtuous Life can make Death Easie to us; Wherefore there's No trusting to the Distraction of an Agonizing, and a Death-bed Repentance.*

139

A Boy and False Alarms

A *Shepherd's* Boy had gotten a Roguy Trick of crying [a *Wolfe*, a *Wolfe*] when there was no such Matter, and Fooling the Country People with *False Alarms*. He had been at This Sport so many times in Jest, that they would not Believe him at last when he was in Earnest: And so the *Wolves* Brake in upon the Flock, and Worry'd the *Sheep* at Pleasure.

THE MORAL *He must be a very Wise Man that knows the True Bounds, and Measures of Fooling, with a respect to Time, Place, Matters, Persons, &c. But Religion, Business, and Cases of Consequence must be Expected out of That sort of Liberty.*

A Father and his Sons

A Country-man that liv'd Handsomly in the World Himself upon his Honest Labour and Industry, was desirous his Sons should do so After Him; and being now upon his Death-Bed: [My Dear Children (says he) I reckon my self Bound to tell you before I depart, that there is a Considerable Treasure Hid in my *Vineyard*. Wherefore pray be sure to Dig, and search narrowly for't when I am gone] The *Father* Dies, and the *Sons* fall immediately to Work upon the *Vineyard*. They turn'd it up over and over, and not one Penny of Money to be found there, but the Profit of the Next Vintage Expounded the Riddle.

THE MORAL *Good Councel is the Best Legacy a Father can leave to a Child, and it is still the Better, when it is so wrapt up, as to beget a Curiosity as well as an Inclination to follow it.*

A Lion and a Mouse

UPON the Roaring of a Beast in the Wood, a *Mouse* ran presently out to see what News: and what was it, but a *Lion* Hamper'd in a Net! This Accident brought to her mind, how that she her self, but some few Days before, had fall'n under the Paw of a Certain Generous *Lion*, that let her go again. Upon a Strict Enquiry into the Matter, she found This to be That very *Lion*, and so set her self presently to Work upon the Couplings of the Net; Gnaw'd the Threads to pieces, and in Gratitude Deliver'd her Preserver.

THE MORAL *Without Good Nature, and Gratitude, Men had as good live in a Wilderness as in a Society. There is no Subject so Inconsiderable, but his Prince, at some time or Other, may have Occasion for him, and it holds through the Whole Scale of the Creation, that the Great and the Little have Need one of Another.*

143

An Ass and a Whelp

A Gentleman had got a Favourite *Spaniel*, that would be still Toying, and Leaping upon him, Licking his Cheeks, and playing a Thousand pretty Gamboles, which the Master was well enough pleas'd withal. This Wanton Humour succeeded so well with the *Puppy*, that an *Ass* in the House would needs go the same Gamesome Way to Work, to Curry favour for Himself too; but he was quickly given to understand, with a Good Cudgel, the Difference betwixt the One Play-Fellow and the Other.

THE MORAL *People that live by Example, should do well to look very Narrowly into the Force and Authority of the President, without Saying, or Doing Things at a Venture: for that may Become One Man, which would be Absolutely Intolerable in Another, under Differing Circumstances.*

An Old Lion

A *Lion* that in the Days of his Youth and Strength, had been very Out-
ragious and Cruel, came in the end to be Reduced by Old Age, and
Infirmity, to the last Degree of Misery, and Contempt: Insomuch that
All the Beasts of the Forrest, some out of Insolence, others in Revenge,
some in fine, upon One Pretence, some upon Another, fell upon him
by Consent. He was a Miserable Creature to all Intents and Purposes;
but Nothing went so near the Heart of him in his Distress, as to find
himself Batter'd by the Heel of an *Ass*.

THE MORAL *A Prince that does not secure Friends to Himself while he is
in Power and Condition to oblige them, must never expect to find Friends,
when he is Old and Impotent, and no longer Able to do them any Good.
If he Governs Tyrannically in his Youth, he will be sure to be Treated
Contemptuously in his Age; and the Baser his Enemies are, the more
Insolent, and Intolerable will be the Affront.*

147

A Fox and a Raven

A Certain *Fox* spy'd out a *Raven* upon a Tree with a Morsel in his mouth, that set his Chops a watering; but how to come at it was the Question. Oh thou Blessed Bird! (says he) the Delight of Gods, and of Men! and so he lays himself forth upon the Gracefulness of the *Raven's* Person, and the Beauty of his Plumes; His Admirable Gift of *Augury*, &c. And now, says the *Fox*, If thou hadst but a Voice answerable to the rest of thy Excellent Qualities, the Sun in the Firmament could not shew the World such Another Creature. This Nauseous Flattery sets the *Raven* immediately a Gaping as Wide as ever he could stretch, to give the *Fox* a taste of his Pipe; but upon the Opening of his Mouth he drops his Breakfast, which the *Fox* presently Chopt up, and then bad him remember, that whatever he had said of his *Beauty*, he had spoken nothing yet of his *Brains*.

THE MORAL *There's hardly any Man living that may not be wrought upon more or less by Flattery: For we do all of us Naturally Overween in our Own Favour: But when it comes to be Apply'd once to a Vain Fool, it makes him forty times an Arranter Sot than he was before.*

149

A Crow and a Muscle*

THERE was one of Your *Royston-Crows*, that lay Battering upon a *Muscle*, and could not for his Blood break the Shell to come at the Fish. A *Carrion-Crow*, in this *Interim*, comes up, and tells him, that what he could not do by Force, he might do by Stratagem. Take this *Muscle* up in the Air, says the *Crow*, as High as you can carry it, and then let him fall upon that Rock there; His Own Weight, You shall see, shall break him. The *Roystoner* took his Advice, and it succeeded accordingly; but while the One was upon Wing, the Other stood Lurching upon the Ground, and flew away with the Fish.

THE MORAL Charity begins at Home, *they say; and most People are kind to their Neighbours for their Own sakes.*

*The illustration to this fable shows an eagle and a tortoise.

A City Mouse and a Country Mouse

THERE goes an Old Story of a *Country-Mouse* that Invited a *City-Sister* of hers to a Country Collation, where she spar'd for Nothing that the Place afforded; as Mouldy Crusts, Cheese-Parings, Musty Oatmeal, Rusty Bacon, and the like. Now the *City-Dame* was so well bred, as Seemingly to take All in Good Part: But yet at last. Sister (says she, after the Civilest Fashion) why will you be Miserable when you may be Happy? Why will you lie Pining, and Pinching your self in such a Lonesome Starving Course of Life as This is; when 'tis but going to Town along with Me; to Enjoy all the Pleasures, and Plenty that your Heart can Wish? This was a Temptation the *Country-Mouse* was not able to Resist; so that away they Trudg'd together, and about Midnight got to their Journeys End. The *City-Mouse* shewed her Friend the Larder, the Pantry, the Kitchin, and Other Offices where she laid her Stores; and after This, carry'd her into the Parlour, where they found, yet upon the Table, the Reliques of a Mighty Entertainment of That very Night. The *City-Mouse* Carv'd her Companion of what she lik'd Best, and so to't they fell upon a Velvet Couch together: The Poor *Bumpkin* that had never seen, nor heard of such Doings before, Bless'd her self at the Change of her Condition, when (as ill luck would have it) all on a Sudden, the Doors flew open, and in comes a Crew of Roaring Bullies, with their Wenches, their Dogs and their Bottles, and put the Poor *Mice* to their Wits End how to save their Skins; The Stranger Especially, that had

never been at This Sport before; but she made a Shift however for the present, to slink into a Corner, where she lay Trembling and Panting till the Company went their Way. So soon as ever the House was Quiet again, Well: My *Court-Sister*, says she, If this be the Way of Your *Town Gamboles*, I'll e'en back to my Cottage, and my Mouldy Cheese again; for I had much rather lie Knabbing of Crusts, without either Fear or Danger, in my own Hole, then be Mistress of the Whole World with Perpetual Cares and Alarums.

THE MORAL *The Difference betwixt a Court and a Country Life. The Delights, Innocence, and Security of the One, Compar'd with the Anxiety, the Lewdness, and the Hazards of the Other.*

A Dog in a Manger

A Churlish Envious *Cur* was gotten into a *Manger*, and there lay Growling and Snarling to keep the Horses from their Provender. The *Dog* Eat None Himself, and yet rather Ventur'd the Starving his Own Carcase than he would suffer any thing else to be the Better for't.

THE MORAL *Envy pretends to No Other Happiness then what it derives from the Misery of Other People, and will rather Eat Nothing it self than not Starve Those that Would.*

A Countryman and a Snake

A *Countryman* happen'd in a Hard Winter to spy a *Snake* under a Hedge, that was half Frozen to Death. The Man was Good Natur'd and Took it up, and kept it in his Bosom, till Warmth brought it to Life again; and so soon as ever it was in Condition to do Mischief, it bit the very Man that sav'd the Life on't. Ah thou Ungrateful Wreth! Says he, is that Venemous Ill Nature of thine to be Satisfy'd with nothing less then the Ruine of thy Preserver?

THE MORAL *There are Some Men like Some Snakes; 'Tis Natural to them to be doing Mischief; and the Greater the Benefit on the One side, the More implacable the Malice on the other.*

An Old Tree Transplanted

A Certain *Farmer* had One Choice *Apple-Tree* in his Orchard, that he Valu'd above all the rest, and made his *Landlord* Every Year a Present of the Fruit on't. He lik'd the Apples so very well, that nothing would serve him but *Transplanting* the *Tree* into his Own Grounds. It Wither'd presently upon the Removal, and so there was an End of both Fruit and Tree together. The News was no sooner brought to the Landlord, but he brake out into This Reflexion upon it: This comes, says he, of *Transplanting* an *Old Tree*, to Gratify an Extravagant Appetite: Whereas, if I could have Contented my self with the Fruit, and left my Tenant the Tree still, All had been Well.

THE MORAL *Nature has her Certain Methods and Seasons for the Doing of Every Thing, and there must be no Trying of Experiments to put her out of her Course.*

An Astrologer and a Traveller

A Certain *Star-Gazer* had the Fortune, in the very Height of his Coelestial Observations, to stumble into a Ditch: a Sober Fellow passing by, gave him a piece of wholesom Counsel. Friend, says he, Make a Right Use of Your Present Misfortune; and Pray, for the future, let the Stars go on quietly in their Courses, and do you look a little better to the Ditches.

THE MORAL *There needs no more than Impudence and Ignorance, on the One side, and a Superstitious Credulity on the Other, to the Setting up of a Fortune-Teller.*

A Wolf and a Crane

A *Wolf* had got a Bone in's Throat, and could think of no better Instrument to Ease him of it, than the Bill of a *Crane;* so he went and Treated with a *Crane* to help him out with it, upon Condition of a very considerable Reward for his Pains. The *Crane* did him the Good Office, and then claim'd his Promise. Why how now Impudence! (says t'other) Do you put your Head into the Mouth of a *Wolf,* and then, when y've brought it out again safe and sound, do you talk of a Reward? Why Sirrah, you have your Head again, and is not that a Sufficient Recompence?

THE MORAL *One Good Turn they say requires another: But yet He that has to do with Wild Beasts (as some Men are No Better) and comes off with a Whole Skin, let him Expect No Other Reward.*

A Lion, an Ass, &c. a Hunting

A *Lion*, an *Ass*, and some other of their Fellow-Forresters, went a Hunting one day; and every one to go *share and share-like* in what they took. They pluck'd down a Stag, and cut him up into so many Parts, but as they were entring upon the Dividend, *Hands off* says the *Lion: This* Part is mine by the Priviledge of my *Quality: This* because I'll have it *in spite of your Teeth: This* again, because I took most *Pains* for't; and if you Dispute the *Fourth*, we must e'en Pluck a Crow about it. So the Confederates Mouths were all stopt, and they went away as mute as Fishes.

THE MORAL *There's no Entring into Leagues or Partnerships, with those that are either too Powerful, or too Crafty for us. He that has the Staff in his Hand will be his own Carver.* Bought Wit is Best.

A Dog and a Shadow

As a *Dog* was crossing a River, with a Morcel of Good Flesh in his Mouth, he saw (as he thought) Another Dog under the Water, upon the very same Adventure. He never consider'd that the one was only the *Image* of the Other, but out of a Greediness to get Both, he Chops at the *Shadow*, and Loses the *Substance*.

THE MORAL All Covet, All Lose; *which may serve for a Reproof to Those that Govern their Lives by Fancy and Appetite, without consulting the Honour, and Justice of the Case.*

165

A Frog and a Mouse

THERE fell out a Bloody Quarrel once betwixt the *Frogs* and the *Mice*, about the Sovereignty of the Fenns; and whilst Two of their Companions were Disputing it at Swords Point, Down comes a *Kite* Powdering upon them in the *Interim*, and Gobbles up both together, to Part the Fray.

THE MORAL *'Tis the Fate of All* Gotham Quarrels, *when Fools go together by the Ears, to have Knaves run away with the Stakes.*

A Wolf and a Lamb

As a *Wolf* was lapping at the Head of a Fountain, he spy'd a *Lamb*, paddling at the same time, a good way off down the Stream. The *Wolf* had no sooner the Prey in his Eye, but away he runs open-mouth to't. Villain (says he) how dare you lye mudling the Water that I'm a drinking? Indeed, says the poor *Lamb*, I did not think that my drinking there *below*, could have foul'd your Water so far *above*. Nay, says t'other, you'll never leave your chopping of Logick, till your Skin's turn'd over your Ears, as your Fathers was, a matter of six Months ago, for prating at this sawcy rate; you remember it full well, Sirrah. If you'll believe me, Sir, (quoth the innocent *Lamb*, with fear and trembling) I was not come into the World then. Why thou Impudence, cries the *Wolf*, hast thou neither Shame nor Conscience? But in runs in the Blood of your whole Race, Sirrah, to hate our Family; and therefore since Fortune has brought us together so conveniently, you shall e'en pay some of your Fore-Fathers Scores before you and I part; and so without any more ado, he leapt at the Throat of the miserable helpless *Lamb*, and tore him immediately to pieces.

THE MORAL 'Tis an Easy Matter to find a Staff to beat a Dog. *Innocence is no Protection against the Arbitrary Cruelty of a Tyrannical Power: But Reason and Conscience are yet so Sacred, that the Greatest Villanies are still Countenanc'd under that Cloak and Colour.*

A Cock and a Diamond

As a *Cock* was turning up a Dunghill, he spy'd a *Diamond*. Well (says he to himself) this sparkling Foolery now to a Lapidary in my place, would have been the Making of him; but as to any Use or Purpose of mine, a *Barley-Corn* had been worth Forty on't.

THE MORAL *He that's Industrious in an Honest Calling, shall never fail of a Blessing. 'Tis the part of a Wise Man to Prefer Things Necessary before Matters of Curiosity, Ornament, or Pleasure.*

The Frogs Chuse a King

IN the days of Old, when the *Frogs* were All at Liberty in the Lakes, and grown quite Weary of living without Government, they Petition'd *Jupiter* for a *King*, to the End that there might be some Distinction of Good and Evil, by certain Equitable Rules and Methods of Reward and Punishment. *Jupiter*, that knew the Vanity of their Hearts, threw them down a *Log* for their Governour; which upon the first Dash, frighted the whole *Mobile* of them into the Mudd for the very fear on't. This *Panick* Terror kept them in Awe for a while, till in good time one *Frog*, Bolder then Rest, put up his Head, and look'd about him, to see how squares went with their *New King*. Upon This, he calls his Fellow-Subjects together; Opens the truth of the Case; and Nothing would serve them then, but Riding a-top of him; Insomuch that the Dread they were in before, is now turn'd into Insolence, and Tumult. *This King*, they said, was too *Tame* for them, and *Jupiter* must needs be entreated to send 'em Another: He did so, but Authors are divided upon it, whether 'twas a *Stork*, or a *Serpent*; though whether of the Two soever it was, he left them neither Liberty, nor Property, but made a Prey of his Subjects. Such was their Condition in fine, that they sent *Mercury* to *Jupiter* yet once again for *Another King*, whose Answer was This: *They that will not be Contented when they are Well, must be Patient when Things are Amiss with them:* and People had better Rest where they are, then go farther, and fare Worse.

THE MORAL *The* Mobile *are uneasie without a Ruler: They are as Restless with one; and the oftner they shift, the Worse they Are; So that Government, or No Government; a King of God's Making or of the Peoples, or none at all, the Multitude are never to be satisfied.*

List of Fables